A Fylde Country Practice

A Fylde Country Practice

MEDICINE AND SOCIETY IN LANCASHIRE,
c.1760–1840

Steven King

Centre for North-West Regional Studies
University of Lancaster
2001
Series Editor: Jean Turnbull

A Fylde Country Practice: Medicine and Society in Lancashire, c.1760–1840

This volume is the 46th in a series published by the
Centre for North-West Regional Studies at the University of Lancaster

Text copyright © Steven King 2001

Designed, typeset, printed and bound by
JW Arrowsmith Ltd, Bristol

British Library Cataloguing-in-Publication Data
A CIP catalogue record for this book is available from the British Library

ISBN 1-86220-117-X

Cover: 'A map of the country palatine of Lancaster from a survey made in
the years 1828 and 1829 by G. Hennet engraved by James Bingley.'
Reproduced by kind permission of Ian Saunders

For Catherine,
with love and now with sadness

Contents

List of Illustrations

Figures

Maps

Frontispiece: John Cary 'Lancashire' from *New and Correct English Atlas* (1787).
First Issue.

Acknowledgements

This book has been some time in the making. It owes debts to many people. While working at the University of Central Lancashire Rex Pope sanctioned the pump priming money that facilitated the collection of some of the material on which this book is based by my friend, colleague and sometimes co-author, Alan Weaver. Without both of them, this project would have got nowhere. Subsequently at Oxford Brookes my Head of School, John Perkins, has given me the space to pursue further data collection, while the Wellcome Trust has provided generous funding. Staff at several record offices and local studies libraries have been outstandingly helpful, notably the archivists at Bolton, Rawtenstall and Preston. The staff at Bolton have been very patient with my constant queries in person and by letter and I record my special thanks to them here. Medical History colleagues at Oxford Brookes have been vital sounding boards for some of my ideas, as have the participants at seminars in Bonn, Dusseldorf, Lancaster and Trier. I owe particular thanks to Professor Dr Dietrich Ebeling for arranging a Visiting Professorship at the University of Trier where some of this volume was written, and to Margaret Hanly with whom many of the ideas explored here have been discussed. Several individuals and bodies have given permission for the reproduction of illustrative material, and they are gratefully acknowledged here and via the captions. Thanks also to Chris Beacock for cartographic services, Ian Saunders for permission to use the maps of Lancashire and Mark Pearson for photographic services. I also owe many thanks to Jean Turnbull, who has seen this book through the editorial process with speed and efficiency and who has offered useful advice and input at every stage.

I have wanted to write a book for this series since I first arrived at the University of Central Lancashire as a refugee from the southeast in 1993. Collectively you have made realising this ambition possible. Thanks.

Foreword

To historians of Lancashire, the theme of ill health is a familiar one. They know of the periodic mortality crises so graphically recorded in the county's parish registers prior to the 1730s, most particularly, perhaps, that of 1623. They also know of the sickness and injury, especially to children, associated with the rise of mechanised industry in the county from the late eighteenth century, which contemporary critics of the factory system were so eager to exploit. And they are only too well aware of the disease and squalor in Lancashire towns that early Victorian commentators portrayed in such vivid detail and which they linked to appallingly high levels of mortality, particularly amongst infants.

Yet appreciation of such matters demonstrates only limited insights into Lancashire's medical history during the long eighteenth century. Numerous matters need to be addressed in order to begin to understand the significance of what is familiar and to both deepen and extend understanding of what is less familiar. Amongst these matters are analysis of changes in ill health over time, of how ill health varied geographically in the county and of how it affected different social groups. Beyond these considerations lie others, including such matters as how people coped with ill health and how effectively they were able to do so. Furthermore, in order to view these issues in context, there are key questions to be asked about how Lancashire's medical history compared with that of other districts during this period, whether industrialised or not.

That Steven King is prepared to tackle questions of this nature in itself makes his book a most valuable contribution to the literature, the more so because, in the best traditions of regional historical study, he seeks to relate his findings to those appearing in the general medical histories. In fact, historiographical issues provide his starting point and underpin his discussion. What follows is a broadly based and telling analysis of health matters in a rapidly emerging industrial region. Continuity in medical practice and in attitudes towards medicine are explored alongside change, showing that what was new was not necessarily an improvement. And similarities between the experiences of the labouring poor and the middling groups in society are examined alongside differences, demonstrating that choice in medical matters was not always exercised.

In introducing the book, it is tempting to highlight some of the more choice extracts from the range of primary material on which the author draws. But to do so would be to steal his thunder. Suffice it to say that primary extracts he uses not only enable telling points to be made, but they also add greatly to the enjoyment of reading, though not always in a very edifying way! Indeed, the book is as interesting to read as it is informative. Furthermore, it provides a great deal of guidance on how research into medical history at regional level can be effectively undertaken, not only in terms of what issues to address, but also concerning the sources to use and the problems associated with them. It is a volume that should prove highly inspirational to those researching into such a key dimension of Britain's social history.

GEOFFREY TIMMINS,
University of Central Lancashire

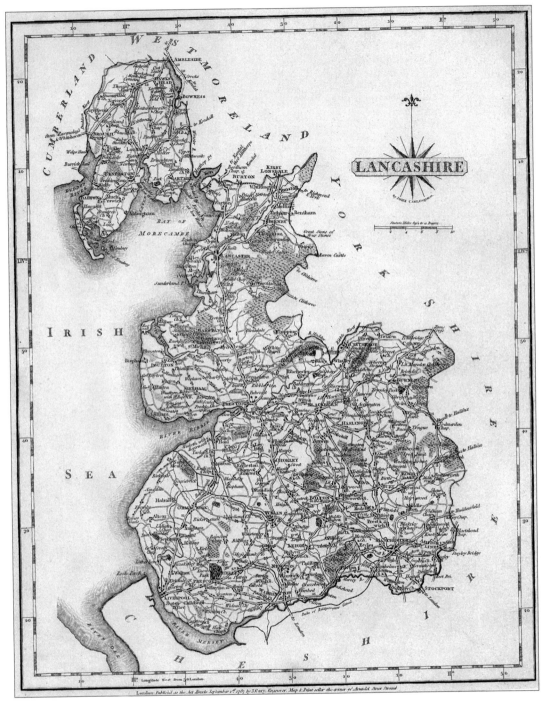

John Cary, 'Lancashire', from *New and Correct English Atlas* (1787).
First Issue. Reproduced by kind permission of Ian Saunders, Lancaster
University.

CHAPTER ONE

Introduction

The explosion of research on medical history over the last twenty years has been one of the most remarkable features of the historiographical landscape. It has bequeathed several core generalisations that must act as a framework for this book.

First, medical historians have come to talk about the development of a medical marketplace in the eighteenth and early nineteenth centuries. Medicine and medical care became commodities to be consumed by middling and even many labouring people, stimulating increasing demand. One consequence was the rise of the surgeon-apothecary and a general increase in the number of doctors, such that, for urban and middling people at the very least, the doctor became a common sight at times of illness. In 1782 there were 3166 provincial practitioners; by 1851 there were 17,491, with 21,146 assistants and students.[1]

However, a *second* generalisation is that trained doctors faced a considerable struggle to assert their professional authority over the dis-ordered medical lives of their patients. Coming into the eighteenth century, the main consumers of doctoring services (the middling and the aristocratic) had few qualms in consulting several doctors during the course of a single illness, as well as engaging irregular practitioners (those who diagnosed and offered treatment as an adjunct of, or supplement to, their regular employment, such as barbers, farriers and butchers), wise men and women, and undertaking their own self-treatment. As the eighteenth century progressed, doctors sought to garner more of the expanding medical market and, at the individual level, to assert sole control over the medical lives of patients. They formed their own trade bodies, tried simultaneously to restrict the supply of formally trained medical personnel and hedge-off the activities of other practitioners, and they subtly changed the processes of medical diagnosis and treatment so that, for instance, prescriptions came to be written in Latin or medical hieroglyphics and treatment came to be framed in terms not of the lifestyle of the patient as had been the case before, but in terms of medical remedies controlled by the professional.[2] Moreover, medical historians have outlined the gradual elimination of the 'patient narrative' (the patient description of their ailment and its causes) from the diagnosis process and the substitution of medical theories or hands on diagnosis of conditions by doctors.[3] Doctors also courted their patients in a social and cultural sense, so that the exchange between doctor and patient would become something more than a simple contractual relationship. The rise of medical etiquette was part and parcel of this and for the early nineteenth century Digby concludes that 'the art of medicine was more highly developed than the science of medicine'.[4] Yet, while most commentators agree that both poor people (because they were forced by institutions such as the poor law and infirmaries) and middling people (because they chose) spent more of their 'ill-health time' as patients of professional medical men by 1830 than had been the case in 1700, the rise of demand for medical services still left plenty of room for the quack, the irregular and itinerant practitioners,[5] and for self-treatment.[6] Even by 1820 it was rare for a single doctor to have the entire medical account of an individual and family. At best, well-informed consumers demanded more than one professional opinion. At worst they doubted the efficacy of the doctors and their cures and consumed quack remedies and their own recipes alongside the prescriptions of the doctor.[7] Through outlets such as magazines, newspapers and published books, medical theories were set alongside quack remedies, old wives tales, the products of chemists and herbalists and family knowledge in the public mind to create a public awareness of 'medicine' which filtered through to all classes. To use the words of Roy Porter, middling medical consumers in particular were 'impressively well informed' and showed 'a relaxed familiarity with the leading medical authorities'.[8]

To some extent the continuance of such medical pluralism is not surprising given the *third* generalisation – that the level of medical knowledge on diagnosis and non-surgical intervention remained strictly limited. In practice, the variety of treatment and its effectiveness changed very little between the late seventeenth and early nineteenth centuries. Despite success in the face of smallpox (which in any case killed relatively few of those who caught it), bleeding, leeches, modifications to diet and life-style, taking the waters and a few basic herbs were still the main weapons in the medical kitbag of all practitioners by 1800. In fact, most advances in fighting individual infection were accidental, as for instance with the beneficial effects of sanitary reform on health. Surgical practice rather than mainstream medical practice witnessed the most fundamental advances in this period and doctors proved ever more willing to consider invasive methods, though their patients did not view the prospect of surgery with the same relish given the lack of anaesthesia or antiseptics.

Related to these observations, a *fourth* generalisation is that processes such as the filtering of access to medicine down the social scale, increasing numbers of doctors and other practitioners, the founding of a medical market place and slow improvements in medical and surgical practices, yielded positive benefit to contemporaries. Medical historians

Figure 1.1: The application of leeches by two surgeons. Source: Item V0016709B, kindly supplied by the Wellcome Library, London.

have come to value 'progress' and, by and large, to portray the survival of older practices and beliefs as backward looking and outdated.[9] As an extension of this attitude, it is frequently assumed that the development of a comprehensive medical system involved leading and lagging regions, with the former (mainly London and towns in the south and west) dragging the latter (implicitly the north and north west) behind it, and with all areas militating towards the same common standards.

These, then, are the key generalisations which will inform this book. Yet, if medical historians can claim to have established the broad outlines of change in the landscape of medicine, there remains much that they *do not* know or have inadequately explored. Did all middling patients engage with medicine and medical men to the degree or in the same way as those, predominantly southern, middling patients who have had their medical lives anatomised? Are medical historians right to place the notion of 'progress' at the heart of their theoretical perspectives on medicine? Is there scope for suggesting that continuity as well as change in medicine was significant at local and regional level, as Porter has suggested? Are medical historians right to adopt market economics as the dominant economic paradigm in medical history? How far and fast did the regime of self-treatment common in the seventeenth century decline? What was the link between the scale and intensity of ill-health and the development of the medical marketplace? And above all, how did long established institutional, religious and cultural structures in the English regions influence supply of, and demand for, medicine? As always in historical analysis the really important perspectives lie in the detail and it is this detail that is conspicuously lacking in medical historiography.

To some extent we are constrained by source problems. The records of doctors have rarely survived, and while the archives of their middling patients are much more voluminous, this in itself poses logistical and interpretational problems. Yet, it is also true that regional archives offer potentially very rich pickings to throw light on the nuances of medical history, continuity as well as change, and neglect of local and regional detail is a matter of choice as well as constraint. This book will begin to apply and question the accepted generalisations of medical history through a wide-ranging analysis of medicine and its social context in Lancashire during the transition of the county from a relative industrial and agricultural backwater in 1700 to a demographic, industrial and urban powerhouse by the 1820s and 1830s. In particular, it will investigate the changing patterns of ill-health in the county, the nature of the response to ill-health, and the changing economic position of doctors. Of course the book has its flaws and it is best to acknowledge these right at the start. Thus, it does not attempt to tell the story of continuity and change in medicine for any particular place. This would simply add one more local study and in any case, I have yet to find any Lancashire community outside the very largest urban areas that might begin to support such a study. Rather, I have chosen to generalise from extensive ad-hoc examples which nonetheless encompass the majority of medical history sources to be found in the county. Map one gives a schematic overview of the main communities from which data have been drawn. Nor does the book provide the sort of in-depth survey of medical historiography that I would have liked to present, let alone survey writing on urbanisation, gender, poverty and welfare and other tangential themes. Space constraints prevent further elaboration. Nor does the book consider Manchester or Liverpool. The medical history of the former has been relatively well considered in the context of the rest of Lancashire and in any case the two towns have too often dominated writing on the county. The dates that I have chosen to begin and end the study are also a little arbitrary, though they do have the advantage of encompassing some of the most profound changes in basic social and economic infrastructure.[10] These caveats notwithstanding, the current study will add to a vibrant medical historiography as well as proving entertaining and illuminating material for those with a dedicated interest in Lancashire history.

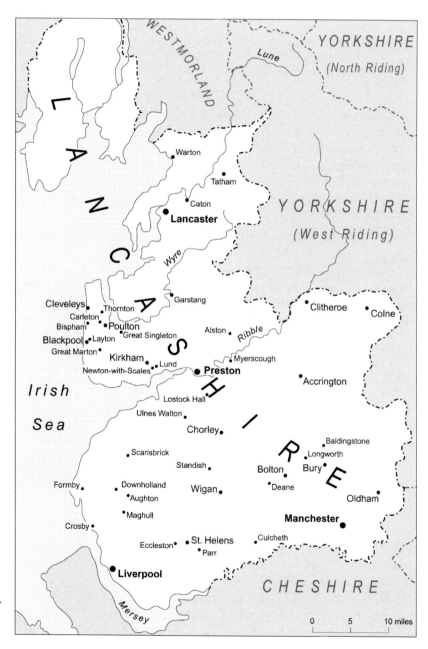

Map 1: Main places mentioned in the text. Map drawn by Chris Beacock.

Notes

1. A. Digby, *Making a Medical Living: Doctors and Patients in the English Market for Medicine, 1720–1911* (Cambridge University Press, 1994). The label 'doctor' hides many status distinctions – surgeons, apothecaries/druggists, physicians, surgeon-apothecaries, some of whom might be licensed and some not – and at the lower end of the profession there was little difference between trained medical men and irregular practitioners and quacks. D. Harley, '"Bred up in the study of that faculty": Licensed physicians in north-west England, 1660–1760', *Medical History*, 38 (1994), 398–420.

2. On the very important point of language in relation to the sick poor, see M. Fissell, 'The disappearance of the patients narrative and the invention of hospital medicine', in R. French and A. Wear (eds.), *British Medicine in an age of Reform* (Routledge, 1991), 92–109, pp. 106.

3. Fissell, 'The disappearance', and J. Lane, '"The doctor scolds me": The diaries and correspondence of patients in eighteenth century England', in R. Porter (ed.), *Patients and practitioners* (Cambridge University Press, 1985), 205–48.

4. Digby, *Making*, pp.310

5. On the latter group see M. Neve, 'Orthodoxy and fringe: medicine in late Georgian Bristol', in W. F. Bynum and R. Porter (eds.), *Medical Fringe and Medical Orthodoxy 1750–1850* (Croom Helm, 1987), 40–55. Also I. Loudon, 'The vile race of quacks with which this country is infested', in *Idem*, 106–28, who notes that in 1804 irregulars outnumbered doctors by 9:1.

6. See J. Barry, 'Publicity and the public good: Presenting medicine in eighteenth century Bristol', in Bynum and Porter, *Medical Fringe*, 29–39.

7. R. Porter, 'The patient in England 1600–1800', in A.Wear (ed.), *Medicine in Society: Historical Essays* (Cambridge University Press, 1992), 91–118, pp. 102–3 and A.Wear, 'Making sense of health and environment in early modern England', in *Idem*, 119–47. On problems of obtaining access to doctors, see G. Smith, 'Prescribing the rules of health: Self-help and advice in the late eighteenth century', in Porter (ed.), *Patients*, 249–82.

8. R. Porter, 'Laymen, doctors and medical knowledge in the eighteenth century: The evidence of the *Gentleman's Magazine*', in Porter (ed.), *Patients*, 283–314, pp. 292. Though see Digby, *Making*, pp.2–3, for scepticism.

9. Though see R. Porter and D. Porter, *In Sickness and in Health: The British Experience* (Fourth Estate, 1988), pp. 267–71.

10. See S. A. King and J. G. Timmins, *Making Sense of the Industrial Revolution* (Manchester University Press, 2001).

CHAPTER TWO

Mortality and ill-health in Lancashire

A thousand ways there is on earth for to deprive poor man of breath[1]

1. *Overview*

The mortality and wider health and ill-health experiences of the English population between the 1700s and 1830s have been the subject of substantial analysis.[2] In their two books on the general English demographic experience, Wrigley and Schofield have established that movements in mortality explain little of the rise in the English population from the mid-eighteenth century. The mortality rates of infants and children, youths and adults had never been particularly high and so their fall could do little to stimulate rising population totals.[3] But fall they did, as Figure 2.1 shows. Using family reconstitution evidence from 26 communities Wrigley et al. demonstrate that after peaking in the period 1725–49 (at 191 deaths per thousand children born) infant death rates fell to just 136 by the early 1820s, rising again after 1825. The latter rise was not caused by precipitous change in the mortality rates of infants in urban areas. Indeed, while public health conditions in some places did deteriorate, the enduring feature of infant mortality on the national stage was the limited rate in market towns and other urban areas. By the early nineteenth century, the chances of infant survival in London and Manchester were considerably better than was the case in comparable cities such as Paris or Lyon.[4] It was in rural industrial and mining areas that high and rising infant death rates were most pronounced. While infant death rates in most places fell after 1750, in these communities they rose markedly.[5] The experience of child and youth mortality (the age groups 1–14) is more difficult to reconstruct than that of infants, but it is clear that by the early nineteenth century death rates in all of the age groups 1–14 were lower than in the 1720s.[6] When we ally these observations with stuttering eighteenth century improvements in adult mortality rates, it is clear that at national level life expectancy at birth rose from 36.6 to 44.8 between 1740 and 1810.[7]

These figures make sense when set against the backdrop of trends in

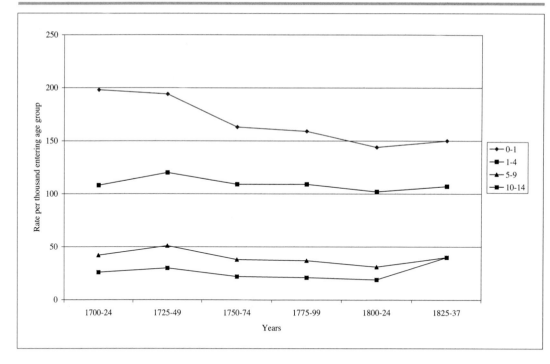

exposure and resistance to disease. The last national mortality crisis (when death rates rise substantially above trend) took place between 1729 and 1732, variously explained by typhoid, typhus, starvation, influenza, smallpox or a succession of smaller epidemics.[8] The plague and epidemic smallpox of the seventeenth century gave way to endemic diseases as urbanisation and population density rose. Smallpox, diseases of childhood such as measles or whooping cough, and digestive diseases, became ever present killers amongst the urban population in particular, only developing into larger scale outbreaks where acquired immunity was diluted (for instance by migration into towns) or where pathogens were taken to areas without substantial immunity. As was suggested in the last chapter, even the impact of new mass killing diseases such as the cholera of the 1830s could be substantially reduced by the accidental elimination of public health risks. In short, the nature of exposure to life-threatening disease changed markedly after 1730. Charles Creighton provides the best general survey of disease conditions in England during the period covered by this book. Using a rich vein of local sources he shows that by the late eighteenth century an industrial town such as Leeds was never free of reported outbreaks of disease, particularly amongst children; however, the outbreaks rarely raged across the town as a whole and absolute number of deaths were usually small.[9] He also confirms that by the nineteenth century, if not before, tuberculosis was the major killer of adults and its effects were much less spectacular than the epidemics of 150 years beforehand. Nor should we forget that the chances of dying from

Figure 2.1: Variations in infant and childhood mortality levels

Source: Reproduced from Wrigley et al, *English Population History*, p.262.

an individual disease where someone caught it also waned. Inoculation (in the case of smallpox), better understanding of the course of endemic disease, the autonomous dilution of the killing power of diseases themselves (particularly malaria and scarlet fever) and rising dietary standards, progressively reduced the mortality risks of becoming ill as measured by historical demographers.[10]

Yet, while there is no doubt that mortality eased over time, the evidence that, at individual level, sickness and ill-health became more frequent and more intense is also persuasive. James Riley uses friendly society data on the number of times payments were made to members for sickness to suggest that between 1750 and 1870 both the number of incidents of sickness and the duration of sickness rose across all age groups. Thus, men aged 50 would have been officially sick for just over one week per year in 1750 but almost two weeks by 1870. Even for friendly society members these figures are an understatement, since people generally had to have been ill for a while before benefits were given. For those outside the friendly society movement, both the incidence and duration of sickness were likely to have been much higher. Riley concludes that 'The modern workforce has gained working life time because the risk of death has declined at each age between 21 and 71. But a significant part of that gain has been counterbalanced by an increase in the duration of sickness.'[11] Such conclusions are logical. If diseases became less potent as killers, getting one might then stimulate another, generating a sustained period of severe ill-health.

These generalisations do not, however, do justice to the situation in Lancashire. As the county was transformed from a relatively poor and sparsely populated area in the seventeenth century to a vibrant, urbanised, fast growing and wealthy area with pockets of severe structural decline by the first decades of the nineteenth century,[12] it is possible that *both* death rates and the scale and intensity of sickness increased. Urban, rural industrial and rural communities in Lancashire had higher death rates than comparable communities elsewhere from the later eighteenth century, and preliminary evidence suggests that industrial accidents, pollution, overcrowding, poor sanitation, a thickening of population in the Lancashire countryside,[13] extensive migration and the apparent tendency for Lancashire people to be susceptible to certain types of mortality more than people from neighbouring counties,[14] pushed up death rates at all ages when national rates fell from the 1740s.[15] In the third decade of the nineteenth century, the sweeping condemnation of housing and public health surveys in towns like Preston highlighted 'the problem of death' in Lancashire. By inference, these surveys also identified 'the problem of health' (or lack of it) amongst Lancastrians, and the rationale for this chapter is to try and uncover the scale and features of this problem.

2. *General patterns of ill-health in Lancashire*

Initially, it is important to weave a general picture of the pattern of disease and ill-health in the county. Charles Creighton provides us with some useful general insights for the later eighteenth century. He suggests that excluding outbreaks of smallpox (which were more numerous than in any other county), cholera and tuberculosis (which was also strongly endemic) five diseases loomed large in the experiences of urban and rural Lancastrians. Outbreaks of influenza, typhus, typhoid, putrid fever and whooping cough occurred over 150 times in Lancashire communities in the last three decades of the eighteenth century alone. As far as we can judge from the Creighton data, deaths from these disease outbreaks were higher in Lancashire than comparable communities in the West Riding, but the absolute numbers rarely reached levels of the sort which we see on the continent at the same time. If people did not die, then frequent outbreaks of disease of the sort highlighted by Creighton must have incapacitated and weakened, suggesting very poor health in *both* rural and urban communities by the later eighteenth century.[16]

Going further than the general picture drawn by Creighton to identify the health framework within which discussion of medicine must be

Figure 2.2: The housing of industrial workers afflicted with TB in Preston Source: *London Illustrated News*, 1842.

framed is a difficult proposition. The parish registers of Colne, which give broad causes of death from 1792, provide one building block.[17] They show just how much of a danger endemic diseases could still pose. Thus smallpox visited the town in 1776 and 1782, when 'The smallpox raged *excessively* at this time, which carried off prodigious numbers of persons, especially infants'.[18] In 1790, the registers note that 'the smallpox was very rife and fatal at this period' and the disease visited the town again in 1794 (when 108 people died) and 1798. Measles killed twenty nine people between 1791 and 1792, returning again in 1793 and 1799, whooping cough was a major killer in 1795 and 1800, and scarlet fever cut through the infant population in 1796/97. Yet, these observations notwithstanding, epidemics were not the major cause of death in Colne during the 1790s. The wider cause of death data, set out in Figure 2.3, is suggestive. Between 1792 and 1800 there were 760 deaths of people aged fourteen or more. Decline (a label for tuberculosis) dominated deaths amongst adults, accounting for over one third of cases. Deaths due to 'old age' accounted for a further 14 per cent of cases, while fevers and bronchial complaints accounted for the majority of other deaths. Amongst children and infants, infectious disease was a more important killer, but even for infants fits and convulsions explain the majority of recorded deaths. Perhaps unsurprisingly, there is considerable resonance here with the observations of Creighton. Of course, we are interested in ill-health amongst the living rather than death, but must bear in mind two points. First, that a number of the people dying would have done so after a lingering illness. Second, that for every person who died of a disease, between two and ten would have the same disease and survive in weakened form. The Colne registers are thus testimony to ill-health on a grand scale.

Figure 2.3: Causes of adult death in Colne, 1792–1800
Source: Calculated from information in Spencer, *Colne Parish Burial Registers*.

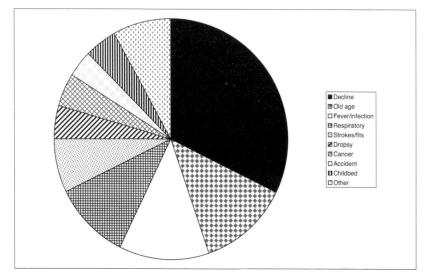

This said, contemporaries were well aware that mortality and disease conditions could vary markedly over even very short distances, so that the experience of one community need bear no relevance to that of another.[19] Social surveys give an opportunity to generalise further. As early as 1786 Thomas Henry urged upon the Lancashire reading public the problems of public health and personal ill-health in the county, noting,

> large towns ... consume many lives, which in their original situation might have continued to exist for several years longer, but are cut off by diseases produced by vitiated air, by infection or by a change in their modes of living ...[20]

Ten years later Dr William Thomas concluded that industry was 'disabling of health'. Aiken took up the theme in 1797, highlighting frequent outbreaks of fever amongst industrial and rural industrial workers and suggesting this might have something to do with 'filth, rags and poverty'.[21] Travelling commentators such as William Cooke Taylor were to substantiate this speculation in the nineteenth century, emphasising that the decimation of household economies by structural and cyclical unemployment could permanently impair the health of vast swathes of Lancashire workers.[22] Figure 2.4 suggests some of the responses to this sort of problem. Even in better times, of course, the physical condition of factory labour and manufacturing districts did not attract much favourable comment. One Lancashire letter writer to the *Morning Chronicle* noted that: 'Men and women appeared to be more or less in a negative sanitary condition. At any rate what is called the "bloom of health" is a flower requiring more air and sunshine than stirs and gleams athwart the rattling spindles'.[23] The situation was not much better outside the mills. Of Bolton, it was noted 'the great mass of the houses are built in the oldest and filthiest fashion. Cellars abound on every side, and I saw few or none unoccupied, while the people appeared to me to be as full squalid and dirty in appearance as the worst classes are in the worst districts of Manchester'.[24] In general, social commentators pointed forcefully to poor and even declining health in the vast majority of Lancashire communities that they observed, the eleven surveys conducted between 1821 and 1837 cataloguing endemic and life-long ill-health in rural, urban and rural industrial communities throughout the county. The parish registers of Colne clearly do not lie, and the health

Figure 2.4: Letter on the distress of handloom weavers Source: Reproduced by kind permission of Bolton Archive and Local Studies Unit.

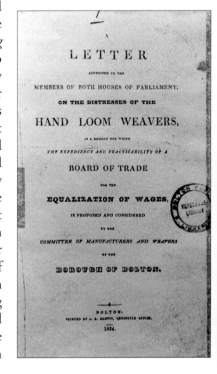

surveys that generally preceded the establishment of infirmaries and dispensaries in the county simply confirm high background levels of sickness.[25]

So, Lancashire was an extremely unhealthy county in a global sense. The key question for this volume is how the general framework translated to the nature of ill-health at individual level. Memorandum books, account books and diaries written by Lancashire contemporaries confirm the general picture of extensive individual ill-health. The diary of Richard Kay highlights the problem of consumption amongst teenagers and young adults, though it was amputation and accident cases, infections, fevers and toothache which attracted most of his comment as he worked in east Lancashire in the 1740s. His diary of 27 June 1743 noted 'we had a patient with . . . the muscle which extends the Thigh cut from Patella or Knee pan by a fall, we had a scrofulous Tumour in the Shoulder with a Caries of the Bone, and Stiffness of the Joint, a strumous Tumour in the Leg infested with Pus from near Ham to Heel, a broken Arm, a Broken Thigh, besides other patients.[26] Conditions in the west of the county were no better. Dr Loxham's account and treatment book for patients on the Fylde covering the middle decades of the eighteenth century is particularly instructive.[27] Figure 2.5 shows clearly that the foundation of Loxham's practice was midwifery services, a common feature of eighteenth century doctoring.[28] However, Figure 2.6 provides a clearer impression of the *range* of complaints that Loxham treated by excluding his midwifery practices. Fevers were the most common complaint, followed by cuts and broken bones and then tumours. The teeth and mouth problems highlighted by Richard Kay in the 1740s and 1750s were also found on the Fylde in the 1760s and 1770s and while amputations make up a relatively small proportion of Loxham's

Figure 2.5: Ailments for which Dr Loxham was called (including midwifery)
Source: Drawn from document DDPr 25/6, 'Account Book of Dr Loxham' at the Lancashire Record Office, Preston.

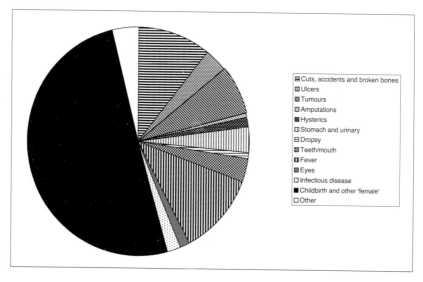

Legend:
- Cuts, accidents and broken bones
- Ulcers
- Tumours
- Amputations
- Hysterics
- Stomach and urinary
- Dropsy
- Teeth/mouth
- Fever
- Eyes
- Infectious disease
- Childbirth and other 'female'
- Other

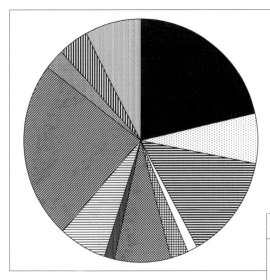

Figure 2.6: Ailments for which Dr Loxham was called (excluding midwifery)
Source: Drawn from document DDPr 25/6, 'Account Book of Dr Loxham' at the Lancashire Record Office, Preston.

Legend:
- ■ Cuts, accidents and broken bones
- ☐ Ulcers
- ⊟ Tumours
- ☐ Amputations
- ⊞ Hysterics
- ⊠ Stomach and urinary
- ▣ Dropsy
- ⊟ Teeth/mouth
- ▨ Fever
- ⊠ Eyes
- ▥ Infectious disease
- ▦ Other

Problem	Number
"Cuts, accidents and broken bones"	143
Ulcers	44
Tumours	92
Amputations	9
Hysterics	17
Stomach and urinary	51
Dropsy	10
Teeth/mouth	44
Fever	158
Eyes	18
Infectious disease	28
Childbirth and other 'female'	682
Other	51

case book, in absolute terms this still meant that nine of his patients had limbs amputated. Body ulcers and strains were also a persistent problem, with Loxham prescribing plenty of liniments and embrocations, but it was relatively uncommon for him to be called out to treat infectious diseases. This may be a source problem as much as a reflection of what Loxham did – some of the fevers recorded may actually have been typhus or smallpox, while it is probable that background tuberculosis went untreated amongst most of his patients.

Moreover, we will see that Lancastrian consumers of medicine consulted a variety of medical opinion, so that it is not at all certain that the full range of complaints amongst his patients would be recorded in Loxham's book. However we choose to interpret the minutia of these charts, it is clear that infection, accidents and niggling health worries were a constant problem for his patients. Many of them had treatment histories stretching over several pages, testimony to this fact.

William Rowbottom's diary provides similar perspectives for the later eighteenth century. He notes, for instance, the experience of his own son: 'This morning James Rowbottom died aged 16 years. He had been *sick for upwards of 5 years* which sickness he bore with the greatest patience and Christian fortitude'.[29] Betty Taylor 'Died after lingering in the greatest agonies ... She was about 20 years of age, had been afflicted with white swellings for upwards of two years'.[30] These are just two examples of seventy or more lingering cases of illness that Rowbottom

Figure 2.7: Letter describing illness Source: Extract from item ZHE/41/11, 'Letter', reproduced by kind permission of Bolton Archive and Local Studies Unit.

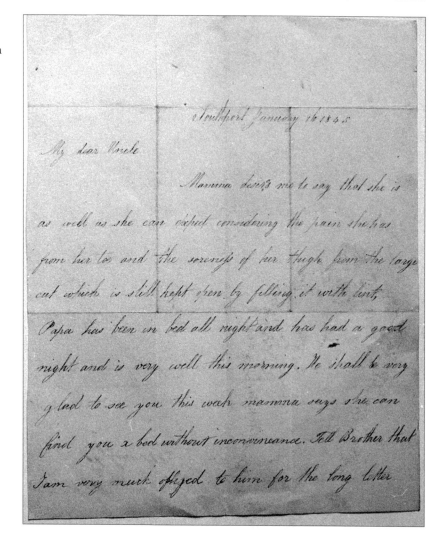

dwelt upon, testimony both to extensive sickness, and a contemporary fascination with health and ill-health that we will see repeated throughout this book.[31] Clearly, concern over sickness was deeply imprinted on the Lancashire psyche. We should not find this surprising. What seem to us minor problems constituted fundamental threats to contemporaries. Simply put, they could not distinguish between an illness that was life-threatening and one that was not. Joseph Ogden of Northmoor is just one of very many people in Rowbottom's diary who died after 'a few days of sickness'.[32]

The diary of Richard Kay confirms that supposedly mild fevers could result in rapid death and that a minor injury could lead to amputation. Even the slightest cold and temperature must thus have been cause for concern. It is also worth remembering that episodes of ill-health and attitudes towards sickness are shaped by the general riskiness of life in Lancashire. William Rowbottom records numerous incidents of deaths caused by collapsing walls, falls, drowning, accidents with machines, transport accidents, accidents during drunkenness, rabies and, particularly, fire. He also records some more unusual events resulting in death. John Taylor of Middleton 'was stricken over the loins with a carrot that weighed 1 pound 6 ounces of which wound he died', while James Garside of Royton when firing a gun had the misfortune to have 'the breech pin flew out and stuck in his forehead'. Jonathan Stansfield of Oldham was also unfortunate. In October 1788 he went on a courting party 'where, he imprudently peeping through the window, received a wound which cut out one of his eyes and he, having the misfortune to lose one before, he is now in a state of darkness'.[33] Roy and Dorothy Porter are clearly correct to note that in the eighteenth century 'death was still seen as awful, arbitrary and absolute'.[34]

Other sources confirm the framework of risk within which we must interpret contemporary attitudes to health and ill-health. Richard Kay's clients and family were more prone to die from accidents than from disease; indeed, the enduring impression of his diary is the frequency with which people fell from their horses and the serious injuries that they could sustain.[35] The Coroner's inquest book for Bolton is also interesting. Figure 2.8 is a reproduction of its opening pages. Between June 1839 and June 1840, 71 inquests were recorded, detailing a range of accidents.

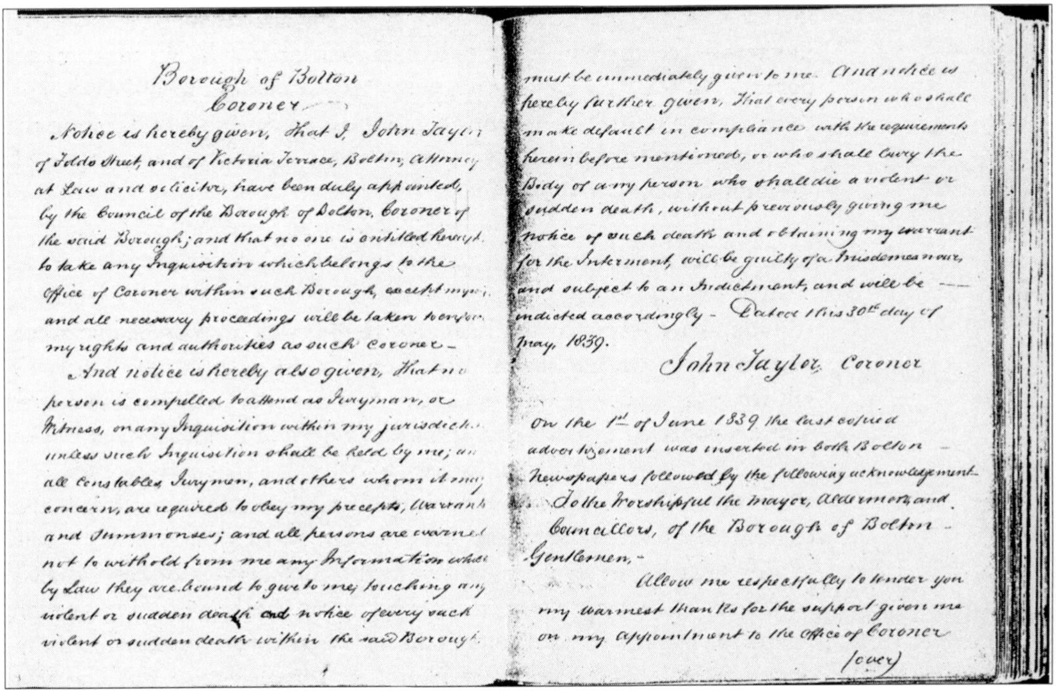

Borough of Bolton
Coroner

Notice is hereby given, That I, John Taylor of Toldo Street, and of Victoria Terrace, Bolton, Attorney at Law and solicitor, have been duly appointed, by the Council of the Borough of Bolton, Coroner of the said Borough; and that no one is entitled hereupt. to take any Inquisition which belongs to the Office of Coroner within such Borough, except my own, and all necessary proceedings will be taken to enforce my rights and authorities as such Coroner –

And notice is hereby also given, That no person is compelled to attend as Juryman, or Witness, on any Inquisition within my jurisdiction unless such Inquisition shall be held by me; and all Constables, Jurymen, and others whom it may concern, are required to obey my precepts, Warrants and Summonses; and all persons are warned not to withold from me any Information which by Law they are bound to give to me, touching any violent or sudden death and notice of every such violent or sudden death within the said Borough must be immediately given to me. And notice is hereby further given, That every person who shall make default in compliance with the requirements herein before mentioned, or who shall bury the Body of any person who shall die a violent or sudden death, without previously giving me notice of such death and obtaining my warrant for the Interment, will be guilty of a Misdemeanour, and subject to an Indictment, and will be – indicted accordingly – Dated this 30th day of May, 1839.

John Taylor Coroner

On the 1st of June 1839 the last costed advertizement was inserted in both Bolton – Newspapers followed by the following acknowledgement –

To the Worshipful the Mayor, Aldermen, and Councillors, of the Borough of Bolton –

Gentlemen, –

Allow me respectfully to tender you my warmest thanks for the support given me on my appointment to the Office of Coroner

(over)

Figure 2.8: Frontispiece of the Bolton Coroner book
Source: Item ZZ/627/1, 'Borough of Bolton Coroner book', reproduced by kind permission of Bolton Archive and Local Studies Unit.

Falling masonry, falling down steps (usually when drunk), drowning in privies, crushing, clothing catching fire, industrial accidents, scalding and a 'visitation of God' took people off suddenly, but for each person that died and whose case ended up before the coroner, several more were suddenly disabled or injured by the same events, ushering in periods of sustained ill-health. One particular case illustrates this well. In 1845, a steam engine at the Bolton firm of Rothwell and Kitts exploded. Fifteen people died (usually after lingering in a period of agony) and Kitts was charged with manslaughter. However, a further 130 people were injured in the explosion, a serious blow to individual and family health in the town.[36]

Much more evidence could have been presented. The key point is that ill-health was a constant feature of the individual and family lives of Lancastrians. Endemic and epidemic diseases might periodically bring death to large sections of communities, but the longer term ill-health which such diseases caused was more important. Moreover, as the casebook of Dr Loxham has shown, apparently less serious illnesses also dogged ordinary people. Fevers, toothaches, ulcers, problems associated with frequent childbirth and accidents were the standard fare of the doctor, and the impression is that such problems were an ever present threat. And threat they were. When life could move to death with such ease and suddenness in an era when diagnosis and cure were limited, health was something to be valued and ill-health was something to be dreaded. Since there is at least some evidence that the frequency and intensity of ill-health increased over time, the later eighteenth and early nineteenth century may have looked particularly bleak to contemporaries. In the next chapter we will look at responses to ill-health. For the moment, however, concentrating on two particular sections of society – the poor and the middling[37] – may reveal more about the nature of suffering in Lancastrian society.

3. *The health of the labouring poor*

A preliminary way into the issue of the ill-health of poor people is via poor law data. On the face of it, Lancashire boasts rich sources. A doctor's bill for Simonswood in 1830 records the attendance of Edward Lashcroft on the pauper June Taylor between 9 February and 27 February 1830. His bill of £1 11s. 6d. allowed for 'large bottle of stomach mixture, an astringent solution . . . large bottle of choleybiate medicine . . . large bottle of tonic medicine . . . bottle of pills . . . bluley plaster'. A unique medical register kept by the overseers of Culcheth in the 1830s provides a similar level of detail for several dozen paupers.[38] However, while such entries tell us that paupers were sick, they do not reveal what was wrong with them. In any case, the Simonswood and Culcheth records are the very best that the poor law has to offer; most Lancashire communities do not have such rich sources. For these reasons, poor law data is best suited to establishing the general outlines of ill-health.

Material for Easington provide a useful starting point. Between the 1740s and 1760s overseer accounts for the parish suggest frequent and persistent illness amongst the poor. In the financial year 1745/46 allowances and treatment during pauper illness cost £9 7d. from total expenditure of £53 and by 1751/52 medical related expenditure was £13 18s. 10d. from a total of £64. Where smallpox overwhelmed the parish, as it did in 1762/63, the medical component of total relief could rise considerably.[39] Such bland figures mask the human face of sickness. Many of those recorded as sick in one year went on to receive relief for several years thereafter, suggesting persistent fragility. The Easington material also provides us with an opportunity to gain an insight into the causes of sickness between 1759/60, when the overseer, Edmund Rishton, gave his assessment of the nature of ailments. Thus, Tomary Pollard was 'Allow'd for a pint of Brandy towards curing the ague', while Thomas Layfield was given relief because he was in an advanced state of old age. Widow Stockdale and her children were given relief because of the measles, while Bridget Lawson had dislocated her hips. Where Rishton could not identify the complaint, he simply recorded 'out of health' or 'out of order'. In total he spent £15 6s. 7d. on medical related relief from a total of £84 1s. These were very considerable sums, and they paid not only for allowances but for apothecaries, medical doctors and irregular practitioners.

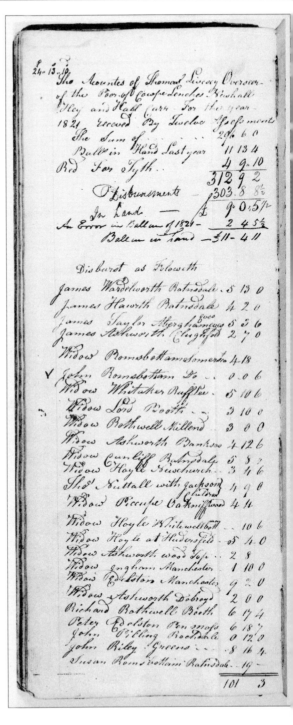

Figure 2.9: Poor law accounts for Cowpe
Source: Reproduced by kind permission of the Local Studies Librarian, Rawtenstall Library.

The accounts for Easington do not allow us to draw clear perspectives on trends in ill-health, but in other places the poor law clearly had to contend with rapid increases in the number of sick paupers. In Kirkham in 1761 only one pauper received relief because of sickness, and the town paid for no professional medical attendance. By 1798 the number of dependent paupers had risen just over threefold but the numbers receiving relief because of sickness had risen to 25 and the poor law paid for professional attendance on ten occasions.[40] The previously undiscovered early nineteenth century overseer accounts for the Kirkham chapelry of Lund also provide excellent information.[41] They suggest that sickness was the major cause of poverty in the village by the early nineteenth century and that poor law authorities were faced with numerous cases of extended sickness. Figure 2.10 reproduces the medical case history of the Parkinson family. The family seem to claim medical and medical related poor relief for a period of well over two years. However, these entries tell only part of the Parkinson story, which starts before 1820, continues after 1822 and contains many more applications for (ostensibly non-medical) relief than are indicated in Figure 2.10. If we read all the entries as a single case of ill-health, then Parkinson's episode lasts the best part of six years and costs the chapelry almost £40. A further seventeen people in Lund were relieved for protracted illness over the period 1818–1823, suggesting (where we make allowance for dependents) that ill-health affected the lives of up to one hundred people over this period. At a time when the chapelry had a population of only 525 this testifies to a prodigious amount of ill-health, something which we see confirmed time and again in west Lancashire poor law material in particular.[42]

Meanwhile, other sources also testify in a general sense to a considerable ill-health problem amongst the poor. The inaugural report of the Bolton dispensary in 1818/1819 notes that because of the number of poor people, 'In few towns therefore are the advantages of a dispensary

Figure 2.10: Medical case history of the Parkinson family of Lund
Source: Drawn from the poor law accounts of Lund and used by kind permission of Martin Ramsbottom.

Date	Who paid	What for	How much
06/02/1820	Dr Taylor	Attending Parkinson	£2 4s. 8d.
06/02/1820	Wm Parkinson	Cash when sick	£5 5s. 4d.
01/05/1820	Wm Parkinson	Rent when sick	£1 5s.
05/07/1820	William Parkinson	Salve ointment	2s. 6d.
24/10/1820	William Parkinson	Cash when sick	£2
04/03/1821	William Parkinson	His wife in childbed	10s.
05/09/1821	Wm Parkinson	Cash when sick	5s.
21/12/1821	Parkinson's wife	Her when lame	4s. 6d.
26/02/1822	Wm Parkinson	Wife in childbed	8s.
02/08/1822	Wm Parkinson	Cash when sick	5s.

more important or extensive than in Bolton'. It went on to warn 'If contagion shall prevail, who shall say "hitherto shalt thou go and no further". The mansions of the great, as well as abodes of poverty and wretchedness are open to pestilence'.[43] This may well have been a marketing ploy to increase the number of subscribers. However, the warnings about the state of poor health amongst the poor are persistently repeated and must have had some basis in reality. In the report of 1819–20, the committee warn 'In every large manufacturing district, and especially in our own, the labouring poor form a most considerable portion of the population and consequently sickness will more extensively prevail'. By 1846 fully 10 per cent of the population of the town were passing through the doors of the infirmary.[44] To borrow the words of the management committee of 1819–20, sickness clearly did prevail. Figure 2.11 is a graph of the number of cases treated and expenditure on drugs. These figures suggest persuasively that ill-health was a heavy burden; they are the more surprising in that lack of funds (the annual report consistently documents

Years	Cases	Spending on drugs (£)
1818–19	2430	293
1819–20	2363	186
1820–21	2295	200
1821–22	2198	199
1822–23	2465	234
1823–24	2578	236
1824–25	2394	267
1825–26	2267	287
1826–27	3306	298
1827–28	3800	300
1828–29	3281	300
1829–30	3364	310
1830–31	3284	298
1831–32	4160	322
1832–33	3927	346
1833–34	4200	374

Figure 2.11: Number of cases and expenditure on drugs in Bolton dispensary Source: Calculated from *The Annual Reports of Bolton Dispensary*, Bolton Archive and Local Studies Unit.

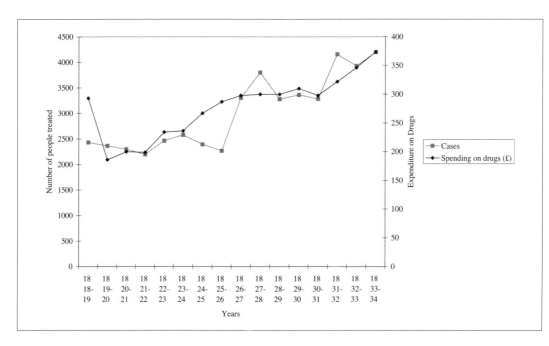

income shortfalls), rules on the admission process and restrictions on the types of cases deemed suitable for treatment, strongly constrained the activities of the management committee and doctors. At best the chart reveals the tip of the illness iceberg in Bolton. In particular, the failure of infirmaries to engage with infectious diseases means that figures from institutions like this do little justice to the suffering caused by the periodic epidemics which raged in eighteenth and nineteenth century Lancashire. William Rowbottom provides confirmation of such events, noting in August 1788 that 'the disorder called the influenza prevailed very much ... and there died some few. They were affected by a great pain in their limbs , a sore throat ... and the flesh wasted astonishingly and left them very weak and low'.[45] With a pressing need to return to work and little opportunity to rest, a single outbreak of influenza could generate a series of bouts of intense ill-health lasting many years and resulting in death. In particular there was a relationship between TB and influenza for the poorest sections of the community.[46]

More detailed perspectives can flesh out the relationship between poverty and ill-health. The early nineteenth century diary of the Preston mechanic Benjamin Shaw is one example.[47] His own brothers, sisters, children and grandchildren were afflicted constantly with fevers and infectious diseases, and many of them died. Tuberculosis took his daughter at age eighteen after a long illness, and his wife a little time after. And his diary sets out a litany of accidents, both to himself, his relatives and those he knew. One, in 1793, resulted in damage to his leg, and from this date until 1810 the leg was periodically lame and subject to infection, such that he effectively had to give up work in 1807 and have his leg amputated in 1810. There is not the space here to begin to investigate the rich archival collection that this prodigious writer generated, but it is clear that the manual labouring poor suffered dreadfully from ill-health at individual and family level.[48] Elite families in Lancashire had long recognised such suffering. In the 1720s, Nicholas Blundell purchased physick, pills, salves and lotions for treatment of the labouring poor of Crosby, as well as making medicine to his own recipe. He actively superintended the dispensing of the medicine and the wider care which the sick required, often buying food and fuel over extended periods. While both his diary and recipe book offer ambiguous evidence on the range of complaints faced by poor people, the frequency with which he purchased or made salves and ointments is probably testimony to extensive skin problems amongst the poor. Stomach complaints and fevers also seem to have been common, and recurring.[49] The Blundells offered medical care as part of their traditional role as Catholic gentry in south west Lancashire. At the other end of the century, Basil Thomas Eccleston of Scarisbrick had only economic motives when he documented the recurrent health problems of the poor. Concerned at the prevalence of fevers, stomach complaints, typhoid, influenza, rheumatism, colds and consumption in south west Lancashire, he constructed a book of remedies to distribute to his tenants, clearly on the basis that they would treat their poor labourers when they fell ill.[50] Unfortunately he could do little for his own chambermaid Mary Talbot, who being ill with supposed tuberculosis and rheumatism took to her bed and

> kept lieing only remov'd every now and then into a chair while the bed was made, but within these 8 or 10 weeks passed, she could not be moved at all, both her legs were sinew grown and her back was raw, about a month ago she filled with a dropsy and this day about 10 O' clock she was seized with a bleeding at her nose wch continued, then she expired . . . she kept to her bed 464 days or 66 weeks and 2 days.[51]

The poor and the labouring poor, even those working under the best conditions, clearly suffered recurrent bouts of ill-health. The Heywood family in Bolton saw their workers have similar experiences, and constructed a recipe book which was subsequently printed. Figure 2.12 is an extract from the manuscript copy. Given the general framework within which the lives of labouring people were played out, it would be surprising if health did not worsen over time, and sources such as poor law expenditure figures provide initial confirmation of this idea. The

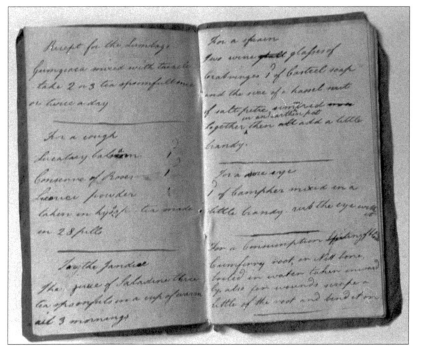

Figure 2.12: The medical recipe book of Robert Heywood Source: Item ZHE/66/42, 'Commonplace book', reproduced by kind permission of Bolton Archive and Local Studies Unit.

middling families of Lancashire did not necessarily fare better, as we shall see below.

4. *Middling health*

Middling health and ill-health is a complicated topic. It is more visible than the health and ill-health of the poor. Middling people were most keen to self-diagnose and most likely to seek formal treatment, so that we can see much of their health lives recorded in letters and diaries. However, such sources are difficult to interpret. Middling people were prone to the notion of health and ill-health as fashion rather than physical condition. The middling hypochondriac was very much a reality, even by the later eighteenth century. In this sense, while letters and diaries provide us with rich narratives, of the sort highlighted in Figure 2.13, it may not always be sensible to rely on what they tell us in order to

Figure 2.13: Heywood family letter dealing with illness Source: Item ZHE/24/8, 'Letter', reproduced by kind permission of Bolton Archive and Local Studies Unit.

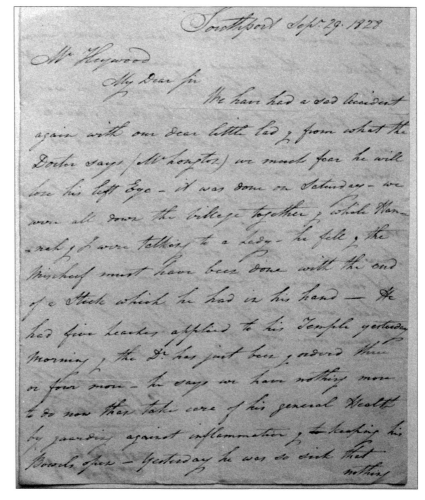

gauge the frequency and intensity of middling ill-health. We should remember too that the states of health and ill-health amongst the middling classes were often likely to be defined by doctors and it is sometimes difficult to see whether descriptions of symptoms and labelling of conditions in middling narratives reflect the opinions of patient or medical men.

Even where we have confidence in the contents of a diary, it is important to reflect on the fact that the act of sending for the doctor is often the occasion which necessitates the recording of illnesses, so that a greater supply of doctors or a greater tendency to turn to them could lead to a greater discussion of the nature of health and ill-health than the physical condition warrants. Nor should we forget that while individual

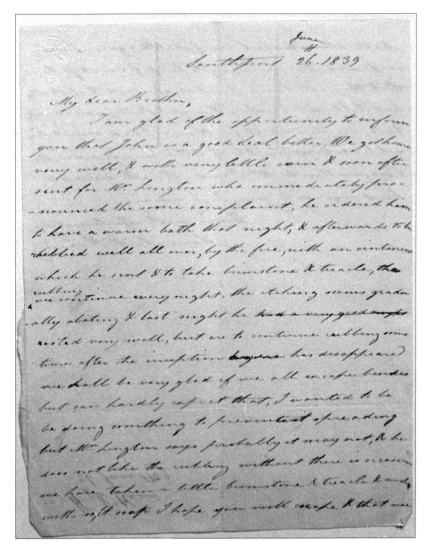

Figure 2.14: Letter detailing illness and medical care
Source: Item ZHE/35/53, 'Letter', reproduced by kind permission of Bolton Archive and Local Studies Unit.

narratives survive in some abundance, the sources to allow us to take a general survey of the health of middling people do not.

Bearing these caveats in mind, it is clear that the nature of the middling lifestyle predisposed such people to certain types of ailment more rarely seen amongst the poor. Riding and shooting accidents thus appear to have been common amongst the Lancashire middling sorts as were heart attacks and strokes. On the other hand, the nature of the middling lifestyle and their progressive flight from urban centres probably meant that they were less prone to other ailments, particulary diseases like typhus or measles which were associated with overcrowding. However, in terms of fevers, smallpox, influenza, rheumatism, household accidents, stomach and eye troubles and sexual diseases middling families had much in common with their poor neighbours. And like them, there is a sense in which middling people viewed illness with dread.

Some narrative examples can help us to understand the middling experience. Thomas Tyldesley of Myerscough and Blackpool was 55 when he began his diary in 1712. It presents a litany of sickness leading up to his death in 1715, including a continuous two month period of incapacity between early November 1712 and early January 1713 as a mixture of gout, fever and stomach complaints succeed each other. As a rough estimate Tyldesley spent one third of his time being what he styled 'out of health'.[52] His friend William Standish of Standish fared no better; diaries, memorandum books and accounts suggest that during the 1720s he suffered no less than 29 different illnesses and rarely styled himself 'well'. Twice he was so worried about the seriousness of his condition that he ordered surveys of his estate to accompany his will.[53] The Revd Charles Allen, the attorney Samuel Jewitt and the Thornton family have also left diaries and letters which testify to actual ill-health on a regular basis, an overwhelming fear of illness and a sense of sickness being all around in this area.[54] The diary of Richard Kay and the letters of Thomas Langton, a flax merchant from Kirkham, confirm that middling people had an *expectation* of uncertain health. Kay's family suffered in the face of fever, and he himself experienced frequent stomach, mouth and other health problems. He rarely passed a week without some indisposition, and his plaintiff 'Lord, Help me to bear thy Discipline as becomes a Child of God' seems to have been a heartfelt reaction to his condition.[55] Slightly later in the eighteenth century, few of the Langton letter fail to reflect on health and ill-health. Fevers, influenza, infectious childhood diseases and niggling rheumatic problems washed over the Langtons and visitors to their house, and the family also faced more serious conditions such as cancer and blindness. Joan Wilkinson's reading of the Langton letters suggests 'There is a sense of the omnipresence of indisposition and of the general insecurity of life, and of crises of life and death arising unexpectedly'.[56] Such conclusions would not look out of place when talking about the narrative of Benjamin Shaw.

The extensive diaries of Elizabeth Shackleton, from Alkincoats near
Colne, provide further testimony to middling ill-health. Entries for 1781 are
particularly illuminating.[57] What is immediately noticeable in the diary of
this year is that Shackleton was constantly troubled by niggling and some
quite serious illnesses which either could not be diagnosed by her doctors
or had a shifting diagnosis. Rarely does a week go by without some
lingering or sudden affliction being mentioned. On 26 January she records
that 'The rheumatism struck out from my feet, heel and calf of my leg into
my stomach, such misery never did I suffer'. Unfortunately, the condition
was to get worse. On 9 February, after weeks of illness, she writes 'had a
very restless night great pain in my heel and if possible the thirst more
violent'. By 13 April she was beset with new problems, noting that 'My foot
does very well, but my poor calf is so horribly feint and nervous as I never

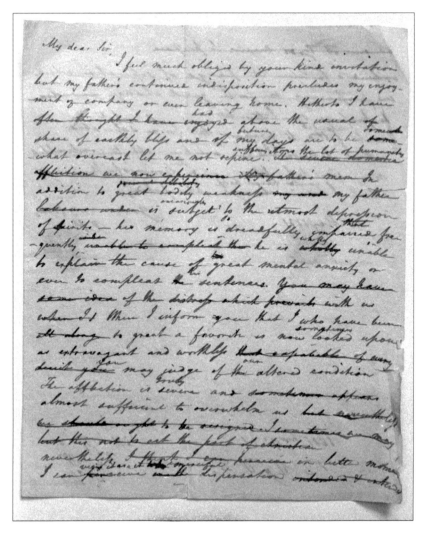

Figure 2.15: Letter
detailing middling
indisposition
Source: Item
ZHE/27/7, 'Letter',
reproduced by kind
permission of Bolton
Archive and Local
Studies Unit.

was before. God Almighty preserve and be with me. 11 weeks this evening since I was taken in this severe and most painful illness'. By 16 April the problem had shifted to her stomach 'I had a most miserable painful night, my stomach very much swell'd, full of wind and cold'. She was still sick by early May when 'I had a most shocking night, never so much violent pain in my foot since it began'. By 10 July she was lamenting 'no strength in me never worse since I began my fatal illness turned of 7 months since'. The illness (which a close reading of the diary suggests to be arthritis and recurring infections resulting from ingrowing nails) was to continue until the end of the diary. Unsurprisingly, Shackleton records with considerable satisfaction the times when she was not ill. On 3 April, for instance, she notes 'God Almighty be praised and make me most heartily thankful I had a fine sleep, composed and refreshing last night'.

We should beware of accepting personal testimony of this sort as definitive evidence of illness given the caveats outlined above. Yet, what is also interesting about the diary is that Shackleton records extensive illnesses amongst her friends and acquaintances, her family and even her doctors. Middling families, particularly the women in these families, wrote to each other and visited each other at times of ill-health. Whatever their own state of health, illness and its effects would have been all around them like a spectre, in a way that modern observers might hardly credit. Ill-health was thus a pressing practical and mental problem, and many of the conclusions to be drawn from the Shackleton material are backed up in other narratives. For instance, Dolly Clayton of Lostock Hall was a prolific Lancashire diarist during the period 1777–1837. Rarely was she well for an entire year, suffering from rheumatism, ulcers, tumours, fevers, swellings, headaches and stomach upsets for often prolonged periods. The year 1802 is typical of many, with Dolly ill for parts of January, February, March, May, July, much of September and November and all of December and the next January.[58] This was illness on a scale not even witnessed by Benjamin Shaw, whose story was unfolded in the last section.

We can end this analysis of middling ill-health with the story of Richard Hodgkinson, estate steward to Lord Lilford. He was an active man who made a point of celebrating his good health. Until well into his old age, he was free of niggling complaints or serious illness, save breaking both arms in a fall during 1825. However, his letters provide a broad canvas on which to trace the health misfortunes of other middling people. Thus, when Richard wrote to his nephew John in February 1815 he reported the illness of his sister:

> Your Aunt Wright is in a very distressed situation. She was severely struck by the Palsy 4 or 5 years ago and about 2 months since had another stroke which deprived her of the use of her speech . . .[59]

Most letters to John had ill-health or death to report. A letter of May 1831 is typical:

Your cousins Mary and Jane have both large families, each having had 9 children out of which Mary has buried one and Jane two. So you see tho' I had a small Family of my own I am likely to have a large one at last . . . I am sorry to inform you that your Aunt is very far from being as well as her Friends could wish. She is not feeble or decrepit in her Limbs, in that respect she is stouter than most women of her Age, but she is afflicted with an internal Complaint, the Palpitation of the Heart, which keeps her in constant agitation . . .[60]

In September 1839 Hodgkinson reported to his nephew that:

Mr Jackson had an awfully sudden death in his family. His youngest son, seven and a half years, was thrown off a poney, his foot sticking in the Stirrup and his head on the Ground. He was dragged off the Poney at full gallop over a rocky surface a considerable distance. His head presented, when taken up, a dreadful spectacle . . .[61]

Hodgkinson's letters to his friends also frequently reported ill-health. Writing to James Blundell in January 1814, he reported:

Of Mr and Mrs Radcliffe I need say nothing, you hear so frequently from them. I am this afternoon going to the Funeral of their neighbour Hannah Robinson, old Betty Jolly's daughter. She had but indifferent health for some time , but she died rather suddenly last Thursday.[62]

In July 1824, another letter reported that

We last week followed our old neighbour Thos. Isherwood to his Grave. He had the misfortune some Months ago to fall down the Granary Steps in the yard at the Bull and has been confined ever since . . . with the exception of the children at the Lodge having the Hooping Cough, my Family are, generally speaking, well.[63]

A final letter in August 1832 tells us more about Hodgkinson's views on the general state of health:

Instances of Mortality among our Friends are daily occurring . . . Miss Crouchley is to be interred today and her brother Joseph is dying daily. At Warrington where much of my Business lies, the Cholera has already carried off above 200 Persons. My Daughter Guest has had a very alarming Inflammatory Attack and from several Relapses is not yet out of Danger.[64]

Whether middling ill-health became more frequent or more prolonged over time is difficult to gauge. What is certain, however, is that, as with the poor, ill-health was a constant threat to early modern Lancastrians. We must neither understate its prevalence nor ignore its impact on individuals and families.

5. *Conclusion*

Roy and Dorothy Porter suggest that 'dwelling on death was ... not a morbid fixation but an honest realism'.[65] Nowhere in eighteenth and nineteenth century Britain was this truer than in Lancashire. Death and illness visited all classes with greater regularity than anywhere else. Youths, adults and the elderly were plagued by accidents, niggling health problems and serious illnesses, with tuberculosis a major killer. Little wonder, then, that Lancashire diarists wrote so much about health and ill-health and that the state of being well was something to be celebrated. The corollary of this observation is that the demand of Lancashire people for medical aid should have been strong and that the county could act as a test bed for some of the generalisations outlined in the introduction.

Notes

1. A. Peat (ed.), *The most dismal times: William Rowbottom's diary Part 1: 1787–1799* (Oldham Borough Council, 1996), 18.
2. For general surveys, see R. S. Schofield, D. Reher and A. Bideau (eds.), *The Decline of Mortality in Europe* (Clarendon Press, 1991), C.Hamlin, *Public Health and Social Justice in the age of Chadwick: Britain 1800–1854* (Cambridge University Press, 1998) and A. Mercer, *Disease, Mortality and Population* (Leicester University Press, 1990).
3. E. A. Wrigley and R. S. Schofield, *The Population History of England 1541–1871: A Reconstruction* (Arnold, 1981) and E. A. Wrigley, R. S. Davies, J. E. Oeppen and R. S. Schofield, *English Population History From Family Reconstitution 1580–1837* (Cambridge University Press, 1997).
4. For other European comparisons, see contributions to C. Corsini and P .Viazo (eds.), *The Decline of Infant Mortality in Europe 1800–1950: Four National Case Studies* (European University, 1993).
5. On this see P. Hudson and S. A. King, 'Two textile townships: A comparative demographic analysis', *Economic History Review*, LIII (2000), 706–41.
6. For a discussion of this point see S. A. King and J. G. Timmins, *Making Sense of the Industrial Revolution* (Manchester University Press, 2001).
7. Wrigley et al, *English*, 295. Also King and Timmins, *Making*, esp. chapter 7.
8. For good local studies, see J. A. Johnston, 'The impact of the epidemics of 1727–1730 in south west Worcestershire', *Medical History*, 25 (1971), 278–92, and S. Jackson,

'Death and disease in Bradford upon Avon', *Journal of Regional and Local Studies*, 6 (1986), 26–34.

9. C. Creighton, *A History of Epidemics in Britain* (Cass, 1965 reprint).

10. There is considerable debate over chronological variations in the level of exposure to disease, levels of resistance, recovery rates and the part played by changes in living standards, public health, the virulence of diseases themselves and improved personal hygiene in combatting disease. See Mercer, *Disease* and then contrast the explanations offered by Hamlin, *Public* and T. Mckeown, 'Food, infection and population', *Journal of Interdisciplinary History*, 14 (1983), 227–47.

11. J. Riley, 'Working health time: a comparison of preindustrial, industrial, and postindustrial experience in life and health', *Explorations in Economic History*, 28 (1991), 169–91. For a wider discussion see J. Riley, *Sickness, Recovery and Death* (Iowa University Press, 1989) and J. C. Riley, *Sick not Dead: The Health of British Workingmen During the Mortality Transition* (Johns Hopkins University Press, 1997).

12. In 1700 the population was 166,000 (or one fortieth of the national population); by 1830 the population was 1,335,600 (or about one tenth of the national population) and population density figures were the highest outside London. On structural decline see J. G. Timmins, *The last shift* (Manchester University Press, 1993). Also F. Vigier, *Change and Apathy: Liverpool and Manchester During the Industrial Revolution* (Masachusetts University Press, 1970).

13. In 1750 there were six urban places within a 20 mile radius of Manchester, by 1821, there were 16 such places.

14. On this see R. S. Schofield, 'Perinatal mortality in Hawkshead, Lancashire, 1581–1710', *Local Population Studies*, 4 (1970), 1–19. However, for evidence that Lancashire people had always been *less* prone to rickets than the rest of the country, see V. A. Fildes, 'The English disease: infantile rickets and scurvy in pre-industrial England', J. Cule and T. Turner (eds.), *Childcare Through the Centuries* (University of Wales Press, 1986), 121–34.

15. For evidence of high and rising mortality in Lancashire towns and villages between 1813–36, see P. Huck, 'Infant mortality and living standards of English workers during the Industrial Revolution', *Journal of Economic History*, 55 (1995), 528–50. For comparable west Yorkshire data see Hudson and King, 'Two'.

16. Creighton, *A History*.

17. For a discussion of the accuracy of disease labelling in sources such as this, see T. McKeown, 'Fertility, mortality and causes of death: An examination of the issues related to the modern rise of population', *Population Studies*, 32 (1978), 535–42.

18. See W. M. Spencer, *Colne Parish Burial Register, 1790–1812* (Colne Parish Register Society, 1972). My italics. The word *excessively* here indicates that smallpox was expected to carry off some people, but not as many as in 1782. The first mention of smallpox in the diary of Richard Kay is in July 1740, when he also notes it as a disease of the young (ie endemic). See W. Brockbank and F. Kenworthy (eds.), *The diary of Richard Kay, a Lancashire doctor 1716–51* (Chetham Society, 1968).

19. See H. Ratcliffe, *Observations on the Rate of Mortality and Sickness Existing Among Friendly Societies* (Green, 1850).

20. Quoted in T. S. Ashton, *Economic and Social Investigations in Manchester, 1833–1933* (Harvester, 1977 reprint), 35.

21. Quoted in J. T. Ward, *The Factory System, Volume 1* (David and Charles, 1970), 144.

22. W. Cooke Taylor, *Notes of a Tour of the Manufacturing Districts of Lancashire* (Augustus Kelley, 1968).

23. J. Ginswick (ed.), *Labour and the Poor in England and Wales 1849–1851 Volume 1* (Cass, 1983), 16.

24. *Ibid*, 84. For sceptical views on the state of housing even in rural factory villages, see J. G. Timmins, 'Housing quality in rural textile colonies 1800–1850: The Ashworth settlements revisited', *Industrial Archaeology Review*, 22 (2000), 21–37.

25. Ashton, *Economic*, 15. See also G. McLoughlin, *A Short History of the First Liverpool Infirmary, 1749–1824* (Phillimore, 1978).

26. Brockbank and Kenworthy, *The Diary*, 64.

27. See Lancashire Record Office (hereafter LRO) DDPr 25/6, 'Account book'.

28. See A. Digby, *Making a Medical Living: Doctors and Patients in the English Market for Medicine, 1720–1911* (Cambridge University Press, 1994).

29. Peat, *The Most*, 55. My italics.

30. *Ibid*, 88.

31. Experiences of health and ill-health provided a core topic for Lancashire dialect poetry and song. See B. Hollingworth (ed.), *Songs of the People: Lancashire Dialect Poetry of the Industrial Revolution* (Manchester University Press, 1977), 116–19.

32. Peat, *The Most*, 26.

33. Peat, *The Most*, 18, 34, 45.

34. See R. Porter and D. Porter, *In Sickness and in Health: The British Experience 1650–1850* (Fourth Estate, 1988), 249.

35. Brockbank and Kenworthy, *The Diary*.

36. Bolton Local Studies Library (hereafter BL), ZZ/627/1, 'Borough of Bolton coroner's inquests, 1839–1847'.

37. Both terms suffer from definitional problems. On definitions of 'the poor' see S. A. King, *Poverty and welfare in England 1700–1850: a regional perspective* (Manchester University Press, 2000) and on definitions of 'middling' see contributions to J. Barry and C. Brooks (eds.), *The Middling Sort of People: Culture, Society and Politics in England 1550–1800* (Macmillan, 1994).

38. LRO PR 113, 'Doctors bill, Simonswood' and LRO PR 2853, 'Accounts'; LRO PR 3021, 'Register'. See also LRO PR 3168/5/1, 'Tarelton select vestry book, 1822–36' for the bills of Dr Burrell.

39. LRO PR 2995 1/25, 'Easington parish records'.

40. LRO PR 797, 'Accounts of the overseer, 1754–1801' and LRO PR 801, 'Accounts of the overseer and constable, 1797–99'.

41. I am grateful to Martin Ramsbottom for sight of these accounts, which are in private hands.

42. See, for instance, LRO PR 2853 1/2 and PR 2853 1/5, 'Culcheth overseer accounts'.

43. HBO 1/10/1, 'Annual report of Bolton dispensary, 1818–1819'.

44. BL HBO 1/10/2, 'Annual report of the Bolton dispensary 1819–1820' and HBO 1/10/17, 'Annual report, 1834–35'.

45. Peat, *The Most*, 23.

46. F. B. Smith, *The Retreat of Tuberculosis 1850–1950* (Croom Helm, 1988).

47. A. Crosby (ed.), *The Family Records of Benjamin Shaw Mechanic of Dent, Dolphinholme and Preston, 1772–1841* (Chetham Society, 1991).

48. LRO DDX 1554, 'Benjamin Shaw Collection'.

49. F. Tyrer, *The Poor Law in the Seventeenth and Early Eighteenth Centuries, With Case*

Histories in Crosby and District in the County of Lancashire (Privately published, 1956). Also DDBl Uncatalogued, 'The Blundell collection'.

50. LRO DDSc 150/2, 'Book of medical recipes'.

51. LRO DDSc 127/2, 'Memoranda'.

52. J. Gillow and A. Hewitson, *The Tyldesley Diary: Personal Records of Thomas Tyldesley* (Privately published, 1873).

53. Wigan Record Office (hereafter WRO) D/D St.E, 'Standish collection'.

54. WRO EHC 50/ M819, 'Charles Allen's commonplace book 1748–70' and EHC 175/ M967, 'Jewitt collection' and EHC/ M786, 'Thornton collection'.

55. Brockbank and Kenworthy, *The Diary*, 56.

56. J. Wilkinson, *The Letters of Thomas Langton, Flax Merchant of Kirkham, 1771–1788* (Chetham Society, 1994), 71. Also LRO DDX 190.

57. LRO DDb 81/39, 'Diary'. For general background, see A.Vickery, *The Gentleman's Daughter: Women's Lives in Georgian England* (Yale University Press, 1998).

58. LRO DDX 510, 'The diaries of Dolly Clayton'.

59. F. Wood and K. Wood (eds.), *A Lancashire Gentleman: The Letters and Journals of Richard Hodgkinson 1763–1847* (Alan Sutton, 1992), 263.

60. *Ibid*, 265.

61. *Ibid*, 271.

62. *Ibid*, 296.

63. *Ibid*, 331.

64. *Ibid*, 343.

65. Porter and Porter, *In Sickness*, 247.

CHAPTER THREE

Responses to ill-health

1. *Overview*

The coping strategies deployed by ordinary Lancastrians in reaction to the large-scale ill-health highlighted in the last chapter are partly shaped by the 'national developments' outlined in chapter one. A brief recap is necessary. During the course of the eighteenth century, the rise of the medical marketplace made medicine and medical services a commodity to be consumed. Middling people in particular became well-informed and grasped the belief that illness could and should be cured rather than simply being borne with resignation. They spent increasing amounts of money on doctors, irregulars and quacks, as well as on their own self-dosing. As the last chapter began to suggest, through mechanisms such as the poor law, access to medical services also began to filter down the social scale. In response to increasing demand more doctors took up business, and in order to secure their position they tried to restrict the activities of irregular practitioners and quacks and to assert their own professional role in the diagnosis and treatment of sickness amongst middling patients in particular. This involved the elimination of the patient narrative, subtle changes in the language of medicine and a sustained attack on self-treatment. By the 1820s, middling patients and the poor were spending more of their medical lives under the supervision of the doctor than had been the case in 1750.

Yet, these national developments do not necessarily translate easily or completely to the local and regional context. Lancashire had its distinctive characteristics that we might expect to have shaped reactions to ill-health. Thus, the middling classes multiplied in Lancashire society at a faster rate than in most other regions, a function of fortunes made in industry, commerce and trades influenced by urban development, and more of these middling people than elsewhere lived in large population concentrations. The number of poor people also increased rapidly, though they were faced by a poor law that was one of the harshest in England.[1] Both poor and middling lived in a county with complex topography and a plethora of religious, economic and cultural sub-regions.[2] They also lived in a county that for the whole period covered by this book had fewer doctors per head of population than almost anywhere else. The exact ratio depends upon whether we include doctors resident in Liverpool and Manchester, but in 1783 an approximate range of 1 doctor per 2500–3000 people puts Lancashire at the bottom of national league tables. The nineteenth century position was to worsen, with ratios of between 1:3500 and 1:5000 emerging outside the large urban areas. West Lancashire consistently returned the worst ratios. Meanwhile, nor should we forget that Lancashire could boast a rich and enduring quack culture. Against this backdrop, reactions to ill-health were likely to have been complex across the social spectrum, and it is this complexity that we explore in the current chapter.

2. *Responding to ill-health amongst the labouring poor*

To some extent the most common response to ill-health and disease was to do nothing at all – either because poor people had no access to medical care or chose not to use it. Joan Lane points out that eighteenth century people viewed illness with 'a stoicism and fatalism' not now seen in our medicalized culture.[3] More public medical knowledge probably reduced such resignation over time, but doing nothing may still have been the first response to illness amongst the Lancashire labouring poor as late as the 1830s. This said, the last chapter suggested convincingly that parishes throughout Lancashire were paying doctors to treat the poor by the early nineteenth century in a way that they had not done in the early eighteenth century. In the 1820s the township of Alston retained Dr Eccles, paying bills averaging out at over £7 per year. Drs Smith and Canning were medical advisers to Bispham with Norbreck township in the 1820s.[4] Dr Hindle of Chorley, surgeon and member of the vestry, both assessed the medical needs of paupers and offered them treatment. In December 1800 the vestry resolved that 'Thomas Morris who has 5 children under 6 years of age and earns about 10s. 6d. per week (they being sick of a fever) have 5s. paid for the present relief and the overseer and Doctor Hindle inspect the state and condition of their family'. By 1801, however, the scale of need in Chorley necessitated the appointment of Charles Hill as an additional surgeon and the engagement of a nurse, Mary Ainsworth. Medical expenditure rose thereafter, and the year 1805 proved particularly problematic for the vestry. Figure 3.1 provides a flavour of the medical expenditure incurred in that year:

Not only did the vestry call on the services of their own medical men, they also sent paupers to Preston. In later years the vestry called on medical men in Bolton, Liverpool and Southport. This was medical provision on a considerable scale.[5] Meanwhile, some parishes turned to medical professionals much earlier. By 1794, Clitheroe had retained Drs Metcalfe and Parkinson on yearly contracts.[6] In the 1790s the overseers of Tatham Fell were paying Drs Bannister, Johnson and Tatham for treating

Figure 3.1: Vestry decision on medical relief in Chorley, 1805
Source: Drawn from 'Vestry minute book', Chorley Public Library.

February 7th, 1805	Dorothy Parkinson be allowed 4s. for present and 4s. weekly during illness
February 7th, 1805	A child of Thomas Partington, which is lame, have 2 shirts with 5s. for present relief and that the child be taken to a doctor at Preston
June 6th, 1805	Ann Bennison and her son of Worsley who are in a bad state of health have half a guinea
July 4th, 1805	That Jenny Bennison who has been sick (as also her child now in fever) having applied for relief to have half a guinea allowed her
Sept 2nd, 1805	John Holt who applied for relief and also the town to discharge a certain bill due to Mr Sharples of Ormskirk for attending his wife when sick be allowed £1 5s. for present relief and also the said bill which amounts to a further sum of £1 14s. 8d.
Sept 4th, 1805	That the overseer get the doctor to inspect the condition of John Partington's wife and relieve them
November 7th, 1805	Jane Cockshead have a further 6d. a week allowed her during her illness

the poor, as well as paying bills to several unspecified doctors.[7] Between 1741 and 1763, the township of Easington paid for 5 different midwives, 4 different doctors, 3 different nurses, 1 apothecary and 1 irregular bonesetter.[8] Downholland retained one doctor (Halsall) and two irregulars (Ratcliffe and Yates) during the late 1740s and 1750s.[9] We should also remember that overseers paid for the sick poor to enter asylums. The overseers of Longworth were by no means unusual when they paid £10 18s. 9d. for John Marsden to stay for 13 weeks at an asylum in Manchester between 1791 and 1792.[10] Collectively, these ad hoc examples suggest that there was a pool of doctors willing to treat the poor, even in remote places like Easington, that overseers recognised the validity of the claims of the sick poor (which is hardly surprising given that poor law institutions frequently caused ill-health, as Figure 3.2, dealing with sickness in Bolton workhouse, shows) and that paupers were willing to accept the intervention of doctors.

Yet, to focus on the role of the poor law in providing direct medical treatment is to understate the degree of parish expenditure on the sick poor. When welfare historians talk about 'medical relief', they include in

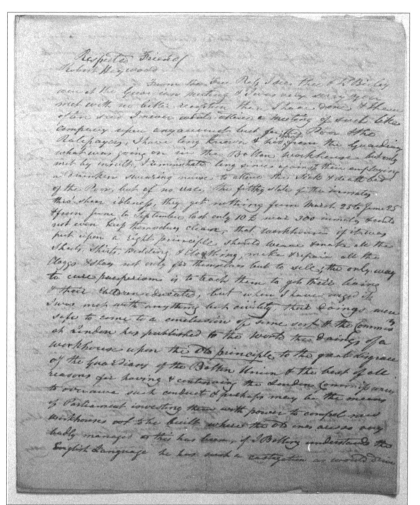

Figure 3.2: Letter
detailing the state of
the workhouse in
Bolton
Source: Item
ZHE/39/29, 'Letter',
reproduced by kind
permission of Bolton
Archive and Local
Studies Unit.

their definition a whole range of expenditure, from fuel and clothing or
food, through coffins and burial duties, to extra pensions. They would
also presumably include the payment made in the Tatham Fell poor law
accounts on 6 January 1790 'for wood leg mending'.[11] Overseer accounts
provide rich testimony to the tendency for even the relatively harsh
parishes and townships of Lancashire to adopt this expansive definition
of the word 'medical'. In Alston, for instance, the overseer faced several
cases like that of James Ireland's wife. She fell ill in March 1820 and was
paid 3s. per week until late July, when her allowance was raised to 6s. per
week, probably in recognition of worsening sickness. In the first week of
August she was given an additional allowance of 6s. but died soon after.
Her coffin, burial duties and food and drink for those attending the
funeral amounted to £2 15s. 8d. and the whole sickness episode (and the
overseers did record it as a single episode) cost £5 6s. 8d. The overseers of

Alston also paid sickness benefits in more indirect ways, particularly making allowances to parents when children were sick, recognition that nursing them involved real opportunity costs.[12] Other nineteenth century communities also proved willing to meet medical-related need. The Bispham with Norbreck vestry recorded in 1827 the case of:

> Mary Badger having had the misfortune to fall from the effects of a fit into her yarn in her looms and so much damaged the same that it cannot be woven we the undersigned do allow her 2s. and agree to pay the damage caused by the misfortune.[13]

This sort of 'medical' expenditure was not confined to nineteenth century parishes, as the accounts of Joseph Sayer, overseer for Easington between 1756–57, testify.[14] Figure 3.3 records the costs associated with the death of the wife of Richard Thornber in this year.

In total, the direct and indirect support given to the family during sickness and in its aftermath had cost the township £14 4s. 2d., testimony both to the willingness of the eighteenth century sick poor to turn to the

Figure 3.3: Costs associated with the death of Mrs Thornber Source: Drawn from item PR 2995 1/25, 'Easington parish records' at the Lancashire Record Office, Preston.

To Richard Thornber by his allowance in his wife's illness	1s. 2d
To Peck o' malt and her funeral	16s. 10d.
To more after wife's death	3s.
To woman attending his wife in sickness	3s. 8d.
To a shifting cloth for his children	5s.
To Christr Walker for his children [they were boarded out]	£3 4s. 2d.

Richard Taylor, overseer for 1757–58 had to take up the expenditure on the family, paying:

To Anthony Thornber 27 weeks board	£1 7s
To Richard Thornber for his second child for a year for all necessaries	£3 5s.
To Thos Howson for Richd Thornber's youngest child 19 weeks and 3 days	£1 12s. 4d.
To Thos Howson towards his [the child's] funeral	12s. 6d.
To Richd Thornber and his child meals	6d.

The situation was still ongoing in 1760, when Robert Blezard was overseer:

To Thos Townson with Thornber's child	£2

and in the year 1762–63 we see:

To doc'r for Thornber's son	13s.

poor law and recognition of the deservingness of those who were sick. Even where they were unwilling to grant direct aid, communities might nonetheless make loans for medical treatment. In March 1763, for instance, Alice Haslam and her daughter Sarah entered into an agreement to pay back a loan from the overseer of Little Bolton 'which the said John as promised to pay unto doctor Bullough for curing the said Sarah Haslam of the French Pox'.[15] Figure 3.4 illustrates this bargain.

These are disjointed instances. Figure 3.5 attempts to take a wider view by charting the amount of medical and medical-related expenditure as a proportion of all expenditure in five Lancashire townships between the late eighteenth and early nineteenth centuries. The tendency for communities under the old poor law to spend progressively more on the medical care of the poor is clear. Given that the Lancashire poor law was consistently one of the harshest in the country, this observation is surprising. We should beware, however, of suggesting that rising expenditure represents a systematic filtering down of the benefits of the medical marketplace to the poor. If sickness levels increased rapidly, as

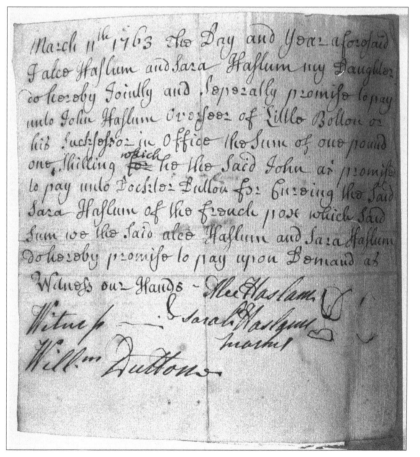

Figure 3.4: Agreement on treatment for venereal disease Source: Item ZZ/238/1/130/6, 'Agreement', reproduced by kind permission of Bolton Archive and Local Studies Unit.

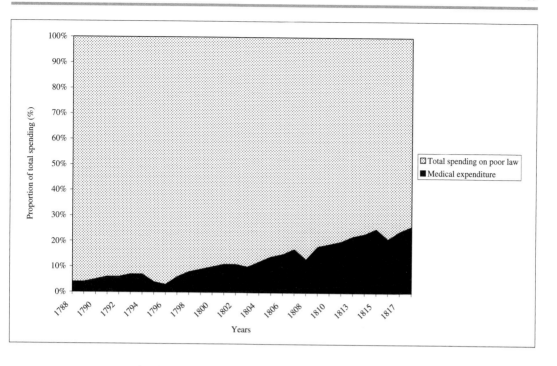

Figure 3.5: The scale of medical-related expenditure in five townships
Source: See text

the last chapter suggested, it is entirely possible that the poor law could offer more aid to more sick people and yet still fail to match the rising trend of background need. Nor does rising expenditure necessarily mean that the claims of the sick poor were always considered pressing by their communities. Indeed, the vestry minutes of Clitheroe and Garstang show that in many cases merely being sick was not enough to qualify for relief.[16] And even where paupers were granted medical aid, the value of being treated by poorly paid and motivated doctors is by no means certain.

For some of those in receipt of medical poor relief, those poor but not destitute, those too proud to apply to the communal welfare system and those turned down by vestries and overseers, other coping strategies for ill-health had to be explored. One recourse was to seek medical charity. The scale of such charity is rarely appreciated. In its most obvious form, hundreds of middling people subscribed capital to build and run infirmaries in several Lancashire towns. Figure 3.6 shows that such institutions had a heavy public presence. Those charged with running infirmaries complained about inadequate resources, while the rules of such institutions often constrained the type of person admitted, as we saw in the last chapter. However, the poor *did* go into infirmaries, a process aided by the fact that poor law authorities often subscribed to them. Starting with Longworth in the 1750s, parishes and townships throughout Lancashire took up subscriptions to the Liverpool Royal Infirmary (founded 1749), Manchester Royal Infirmary (founded 1752) and Lancaster Infirmary (founded 1781). Poor law authorities also helped to underwrite the cost of dispensaries, which had an overwhelmingly poor labouring clientele. Downholland, Formby and Maghull were contributing to the Liverpool Dispensary (established in 1778) by 1781, and dispensaries in Manchester (1790), Ormskirk (1797) and Wigan (1798), attracted similar support from surrounding parishes.[17] Some of these voluntary hospitals and dispensaries were very large indeed. By 1796 the Liverpool Dispensary employed 6 physicians, 3 surgeons and an apothecary, had an annual income of £700 from 360 subscribers and dealt with over 13,000 cases.[18] In 1816–17, the Preston Dispensary had a committee of 6 doctors and 4 apothecaries and employed an uncertain number of apprentices. It treated 2,156 patients and paid out the best part of £200 on drugs and instruments alone. Of course, these numbers tell us little about the standards of medical care available. Scandals at the Preston dispensary suggest that the doctors on the committee were irregular supervisors of the health of the poor and that most treatment and some diagnosis was delegated to apothecaries and apprentices. This is a timely reminder that 'new' does not always mean 'better'.[19]

Poor labouring people who were ineligible for, or not willing to risk, institutional charity, could take advantage of less formal charitable alternatives. The Bolton Benevolent Society spent £4 9s. on medicines and nursing for sick paupers between 1798–1800, in addition to giving allowances and clothing to sick people. It warned subscribers that 'It should be remembered (especially when the sick and distressed belong to distant parishes) that to procure relief for them is often impractical, always difficult and at best inadequate'.[20] Similar sentiments drove the Ladies Lying-in charities in Bolton and Preston, which by the early nineteenth century were paying £60 per year for apothecaries to treat 170 poor women in the aftermath of childbirth.[21] Figure 3.7 reproduces

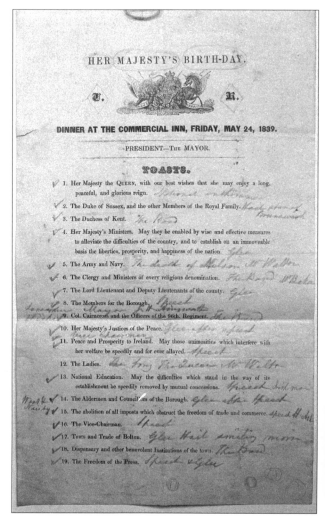

Figure 3.6: Toast showing the visibility of charitable medical institutions
Source: Item ZHE/35/52, 'Toast', reproduced by kind permission of Bolton Archive and Local Studies Unit.

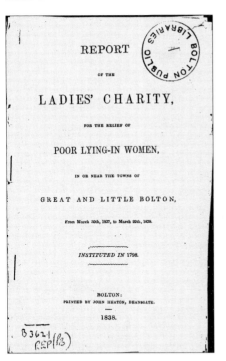

REPORT

OF THE

LADIES' CHARITY,

FOR THE RELIEF OF

POOR LYING-IN WOMEN,

IN OR NEAR THE TOWNS OF

GREAT AND LITTLE BOLTON,

From March 30th, 1837, to March 29th, 1838.

INSTITUTED IN 1798.

BOLTON:
PRINTED BY JOHN HEATON, DEANSGATE.

1838.

Figure 3.7: Report of the Ladies Lying-in Charity for Bolton Source: Private collection.

the front cover of one of the annual reports of the Bolton Society.

Individuals also gave generously and directly to the sick poor on an ad hoc basis. Frances Bankes, for instance, gave cloth and cash to the sick poor from the 1790s, sometimes commenting on the parlous physical state of those coming to the door seeking aid.[22] And, as the last chapter began to suggest, medical charity might actually extend to direct provision of medicines or recipes. However, medical charity did not just flow from the middling classes. Poorer people in Lancashire communities might also subscribe to meet the needs of a particular case of ill-health. One subscription raised in Chorley for 'Mathias Kerfoot towards defraying the expenses of going to Dr Chadwick of Wigan or some other experienced doctor' listed Kerfoot's employer, two of the local suppliers and 36 of his work colleagues. The subscription raised £2 6s. 11d.[23] While only the briefest flavour can be given here, medical charity was everywhere in Lancashire and the sick poor were as much a spur to the charitable imperative as was the uneducated child. Indeed, medical charity may well turn out to be one of the most distinctive forms of medical provision for the poor in the north west.

Of course, some people were unlikely ever to seek charity. Some did not need to because they had insured against the effects of illness through subscriptions to friendly societies or dedicated 'sickness societies'. Where such institutions were on a firm financial footing, they offered benefits which amounted to a substantial portion of the average male daily wage, and most societies retained the services of medical people. The Sick Society of Accrington is a good example.[24] In Bury, a population of 4500 in the 1790s supported ten friendly societies with around 1000 members. One – Bury Women's Friendly Society – was established to pay confinement, sickness and widow benefits to working women, and another – Bury parish church sunday school sick society – confined itself only to children and young people.[25] Some poor law authorities requested certificates from friendly society members who they feared might slip into poverty occasioned by sickness, and such collections demonstrate forcefully that a wide section of the Lancastrian population sought to insure against ill-health by the early nineteenth century.[26] Indeed, the density of friendly society membership in Lancashire was so far ahead of that recorded anywhere else that it must be the case that such mutual institutions were more important providers of medical aid by 1820 than the Lancashire poor law.[27]

Yet, as Collier makes plain, many could not afford the luxury of insurance, even at the peak of their earning careers.[28] For them, and for those like Irish migrants who were effectively excluded from most forms of organised provision, alternative avenues had to be found. Direct recourse to medical people was a possibility. This might take place at several levels. In its most informal sense wise men and women might be engaged to provide medical care. While commentators such as Chamberlain are sceptical about the value of this tactic, stressing that urbanisation divorced wise women from their social and herb base so that charms and ceremonies remained but true medical value was lost, such conclusions perhaps overstate the speed or scale of decline in Lancashire.[29] Access to herbs in urban areas remained easy and cheap, facilitated by the rise of professional herb dealers and growers and artisan botanists.[30] And while it is difficult to pin down their changing role in medical care, it is notable that in the local newspapers of west Lancashire in particular references to this group of practitioners are still to be found in the 1830s. More formally, of course, irregulars practitioners could be a port of call for poor people. Benjamin Shaw went to see the Whitworth Doctors in Rochdale to try and cure an ulcerous leg and he was just one of many poor people who made this journey.[31] And while the Whitworth doctors may be the most famous Lancashire example of irregular practice, there were many more. At one end of the county, in Tatham Fell, Julius Gloxer was an irregular practitioner and local butcher to whom the poor could turn. Even the poor law on occasion turned to him, paying 2s. for treating Wm Borne in December 1789.[32] At the other end of the county, in Worsley, William Hill was a blacksmith who obtained local fame by brewing his own fever medicine which he dispensed on a Saturday to the needy poor.[33] Nor should we forget that professional medical men might offer medical treatment to the poor either at reduced rate or free of charge, a theme that we pick up on in the next chapter.

Above all, however, Lancashire offered the sick poor quacks in abundance.[34] Medical and regional historians have rarely appreciated the extent to which quack remedies had fixed and travelling outlets all over the county. Figure 3.8 reproduces an early nineteenth century advertisement for quack medicines – in this case 'Genuine Daffey's Cordial Elixir' – demonstrating clearly the supply of such patent remedies through a network of fixed and non-specialist shops in Lancaster and Lancashire north of the sands. Patent remedies sold through people other than quacks was also a practice to be found in south east Lancashire. A rare flyer preserved in Bolton Local Studies Library notes that:

Sold by Thomas [crossed out to read Jane] Butter bookseller near St Martin's Lane . . . where (besides books and stationary wares of all sorts)

> is sold the best mathematical and sea instruments, several sorts of physical medicines, as Dr Daffy's Elixir, Stoughton's Elixir, Stomachicum, spirit of scurvy grass golden or plain . . . by wholesale or retail.[35]

It was clearly not difficult to get quack remedies in Bolton. More importantly, Jane Butter appears to have acted as a wholesale merchant, so that anybody could buy remedies and travel around or take temporary shops. Against this backdrop, it is unsurprising that Lancashire was criss-crossed throughout the eighteenth and early nineteenth centuries by a network of itinerant quacks. Such people used flyers too, and some have been preserved. Thus, a travelling quack came to Hulton in 1770. His flyer claimed:

be view'd at, or any time before the Sale.

This is to give Notice.

THE TRUE DAFFY'S ELIXIR

BEWARE of COUNTERFEITS

THat the true Genuine Daffey's Cordial Elixir Salutis, which is only Sold in Kendal by Thomas Aſhburner, at his Printing-Houſe in the Fiſh-Market, and David Harker on the Fellſide, Mr Robert Wharton Joyner in Kirkland, Mr. Beethom in Burton, Mr. Mackrith, Bookſeller in Lancaſter, Mr. Bare in Cartmell Mr. William Bordley Draper in Hawkſhead, being found the moſt Sovereign Remedy made uſe of in the Fevers and Agues, and alſo experienc'd to be a great Preſervative againſt any infectious Diſtemper, if taken now and then by way of Prevention when in Health. This is to inform the Publick, that a large and freſh Parcel of that Excellent Cordial, truly prepared in London, is lately come to Thomas Aſhburner's Printing-houſe in the Fiſh-Market in Kendal aforeſaid, where only 'tis Sold by Wholeſale or Retale. The great Numbers of Counterfeits made in Imitation of this Elixir, are undeniable Proofs of it's being truly Genuine; as alſo the vaſt Numbers of Cures, daily perform'd by it, ſhews it's admirable Worth and excellency. To prevent being impoſed on, carefully mind that the Bottles are ſealed with the above Coat of Arms, and not with a Bucks-Head, or Lion.

The Price of each Bottle is 2 s. 6 d. the large, and 1 s. 3 d. the ſmall Bottle, with printed Books of Cures, given gratis of the many Cures done by the ſaid Elixir.

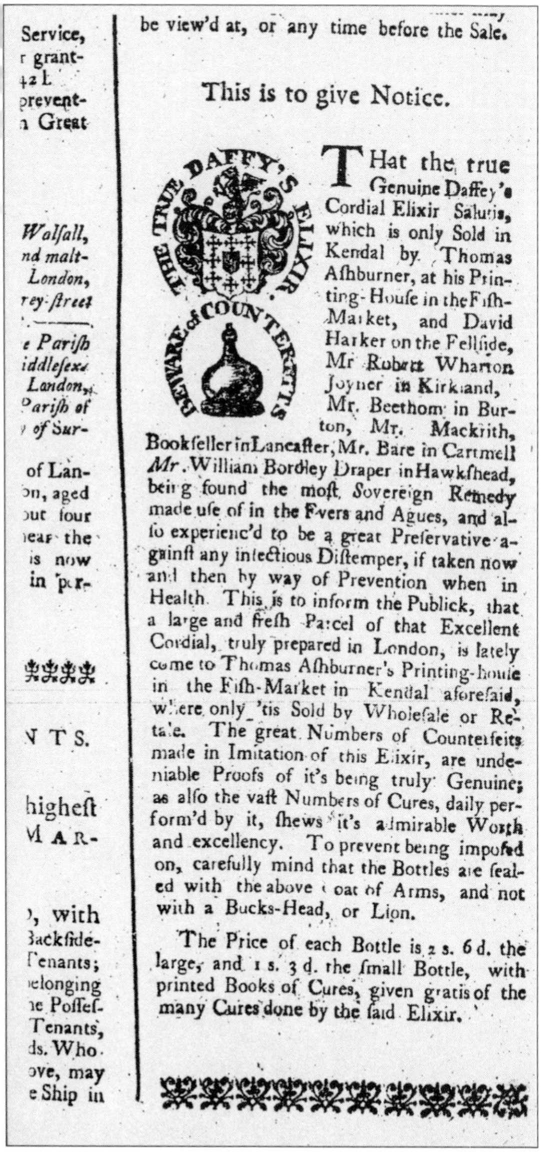

Figure 3.8: Quack flyer
Source: Private collection

> For the good of the public to this place is come by His Majesty's Royal Authority . . . The following medicines are faithfully prepared by Dr M'Layman, surgeon in the army who by god's direction cures the various disorders incident to the Human body and has hitherto met great success in performing many cures, which have been effected with the following medicine. The infallible Balsam of Life which perfectly cures asthmas, coughs and shortness of breath, is of service in relieving the pains of the Gout, rheumatism and other grievous disorders . . . I Thos Abrams – School-master in Leeds, having a great weakness in my stomach and trying the hospitals inn London without any effect for two years, but in purchasing a bottle of Dr M'Layman's Balsam of Life and taking a few drops found myself greatly relieved . . . Witness my Hand [Signature of Abrams]. *Please to keep this bill till called for . . .*[36]

The reference to London hospitals was clearly meant to impress distant Lancastrians, but the key part of this flyer is the last sentence, where it becomes clear that quacks went from door to door selling their wares, probably to middling and poor families alike.

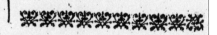

Similar evidence can be found for Blackburn, which was overrun by quack wholesalers and retailers if we are to believe local newspapers, and for Bury, home of the most famous of all Lancashire quacks, Alfred Crompton.[37] Chemists were also active in concocting a distinctive Lancastrian brand of quack remedies, as evidence from surviving bottles has shown. The most famous Lancashire quack remedy of all – Cordial Balm of Gilead – was mixed and sold by the eighteenth century Liverpool-cum-Preston quack chemist, Dr Samuel Solomon.[38] However, poor patients were not confined to quack medicines in Lancashire. A flyer preserved in the Hulton family collection reads:

By his majesty's Royal Letter Patent – Yeakes Justly Famous Pill

Deafness and noises of the head and diseases of the ear if ever so inveterate or long standing are successfully treated at The Hermitage, No. 21 Edgeware road, London, opposite Fisher's Nursery where the names, cases and residency of many respectable persons that have been cured may be seen . . . As above may also be had A Specific Tincture for the Rheumatism, Lumbagao, Sciatica, Cramp, Spasm etc. In these painful and hitherto supposed incurable disorders this celebrated medicine will be found to stand unrivalled as the trial of a single bottle will sufficiently prove . . . Person's stating their cases by letter, addressed to the hermitage, as above, will have the medicines forwarded, with every information required, without any additional expense.[39]

Demand for quack medicines clearly increased markedly over the eighteenth century, and in part this must have reflected purchases by the poor.

Overlapping with quack remedies, there is also evidence that the labouring poor were active in self-diagnosis and treatment using herbal recipes. Where they had the medical support of prominent local families, in places where published diagnosis and treatment books were readily available[40] or where bodies like health boards were disseminating information,[41] this strategy could be very effective. The recipe book kept by Benjamin Shaw, the Lancashire mechanic, is a unique example of self-dosing amongst the labouring poor. His recipes range from the clearly quack such as 'Universal Powder for child disorders':

Take white magnesia 6 drams, cinnabar antimony 2 scruples, mix to a fine powder. This powder will not only prevent but relieve all disorders that arise from acidities in the stomach which children are liable to. This is preferable to any medicine yet known for children cutting their teeth and sickness of the stomach. The dose is from ten grains to half a dram more or less twice a day.[42]

to the superstitious:

> To cure jaundice without physick. Take the patient's morning water and put it into a bottle and take a small piece of saffron and tie it up in a fine piece of muslin and put it into the urine and order the patient to drink neither milk nor malt liquor for a month.[43]

Most of the remedies, however, relate to the everyday problems likely to have been faced by the labouring poor. His remedy for the early stages of consumption was:

> Take the tops of hoe harriot and rye of each a handful and 2 pounds of coarse sugar and put them in 2 quarts of soft water and boil half away, strain it and take 3 tablespoonfuls in the morning, fasting for some time.

For piles, Shaw's book suggested:

> Keep your body gently open with equal parts of cream of tartar and flowers of Brimstone mixt in treacle (or milk) and sit over the steam of hot water poured on the scraps of leather from the cobbler's shop. If necessary use an ointment made of pile wort.

Other remedies may have had particular efficacy. His lineament for scalds and burns recommended 'take a cup full of linseed oil and half as much lime water and threepennyworths of the extract of lead and shake thoroughly'. His cure for fever may also have had some medical substance. He recommended:

> Take of snake root 15 grammes, Cadir [chopped willow bark] 10 grains, sulphur 3 grams, syrup of sugar to mix, and make them into a bolus . . . given in the worst kind of malignant fevers, extended with convulsions and diahorea . . . If plentifully prescribed it requires to be well diluted with small liquor, it will cause a sweat.

This is just a small sample of Benjamin Shaw's writing and it is little wonder that he kept such a book given his own persistent ill-health highlighted in the last chapter. Its wider significance is uncertain. While some of the recipes are clearly drawn from published medical books, the provenance of many of the recipes is unknown, and nor is it clear how long the book was in the making. The medical efficacy of many of the recipes is also uncertain and it is difficult to discern whether Shaw himself, let alone anyone else, actually used them. Certainly, the Shaw collection is voluminous and contains observations of the times, food recipes and other items which suggest that he picked up and recorded the unusual whenever he could. However, the very fact that Shaw kept his book is testimony to a wider interest in self-help. What is more, other parts of the Shaw collection contain detailed descriptions of herbs and their uses for medical conditions.[44] Since these descriptions are not to be found in any of the published eighteenth and early nineteenth century literature still in existence, it is likely that these descriptions were medical tips collected from the neighbourhood or practical experience. And if we do not have the evidence to explore the typicality of Benjamin Shaw, the proliferation of quacks in the county must mean that working class people came to be substantial consumers of the quack remedy and presumably other self-dosed medicines.

This is a brief review of the responses of the poor to ill-health. The number of avenues open to the sick poor clearly increased over time, and there can be little doubt that directly or indirectly, through the poor law and formalised medical charity, more of the lives of poor people came to be played out under the gaze of the medical profession widely defined. This is precisely what the medical historiography would lead us to expect. However, we also witness continuity as well as change in the medical strategies of the Lancashire poor. If they turned in larger numbers to the poor law, they also retained a solid belief in self-help, diagnosing and dosing themselves and insuring against some of the consequences of ill-health via the friendly society movement. And while the poor no doubt accepted the medical interventions of doctors, they must also have spent considerable sums on quack remedies as an adjunct to such treatment or in substitution of it. There were, in other words, significant and enduring regional characteristics in the response to ill-health amongst the poor.

3. Responding to ill-health amongst the middling

The response of middling people to illness was no less diverse than that amongst the Lancashire poor, though the combination of avenues explored might differ radically over time. As with the poor, middling families inherited from the late seventeenth and early eighteenth centuries a rich tradition of doing nothing very much in the face of illness, but of bearing it with resignation and a belief in God's will.[45] This was largely a matter of choice, where similar attitudes amongst the labouring poor at the same time were a matter of necessity.[46] Some Lancashire middling families rapidly threw off this non-interventionist approach as the eighteenth century progressed, though most retained the language of resignation and a belief in the will of God. Richard Kay is a particularly good example of the way in which religious belief and intervention could be combined.[47] So is Elizabeth Shackleton; as the last chapter suggested, almost all of her commentary on illness and 'wellness' was accompanied by prayers to God. However, other families continued to adopt a strictly non-interventionist approach. The Langton family from Kirkham called upon the services of Dr Clayton in the 1770s and 1780s, but they did so infrequently and after much consideration. Thomas Langton generally waited for even serious ailments to take their course, occasionally self-dosing to help them along, and sought comfort in prayers rather than the doctor. His correspondence, as with that of many other families in the west of Lancashire, is full of terms such as 'patience', 'fortitude' and 'resignation', testimony to a considerable degree of continuity in middling responses to ill-health in this part of the county.[48]

Another seventeenth century middling response to ill-health retained its force for rather longer and more universally. Thus, middling Lancashire diarists like Elizabeth Shackleton clearly believed in the link between illness and wellness and life-style. She worried about the impact on her health of late nights, leaking windows, diet, arguments with her husband and family, the weather and even the location of her house.[49] Such continued concern with life-style as part of diagnosis and treatment is perhaps not surprising. Lancashire doctors appear to have retained an interest in the patient narrative for much longer than elsewhere, and to have concentrated on life-style for longer as a consequence. Elizabeth Shackleton's doctor had plenty to say on life-style, as did Dr William St Clare when dealing with her relatives, the Parkers. When Thomas Parker's son was ill with 'pleuritic fever', St Clare waited for him to be well enough to travel and then 'I have advised a change of air and that Mrs Parker may take him upon Tuesday or Wednesday if he continues recovering so fast as he has done'.[50] In his dealings with other parts of the Shackleton-Parker network, St Clare also periodically engaged with life-style. In June 1820 he suggested to the Whitackers of Simonstone that they spend some time at Lytham, renting a cottage on their behalf to facilitate this.[51] On 7 November 1820, when fever threatened one of the Whitacker children, he wrote 'The confinement to which you must have been subjected by the very unfavourable state of the weather, must have in some measure contributed to this attack' and he recommended a trip to the seaside, simplification of diet, increased exercise and the benefits of early rising.[52] Evidence from the Langton papers suggests that Thomas Langton too valued life-style changes as a response to ill-health.[53]

Yet, as one might expect from the national historiography, doctors also became more important purveyors of medical care to middling families during the eighteenth century. While early eighteenth century Lancashire families like the Standishes, Parkers, Whiteheads and Nixons called doctors only infrequently compared to the intensity and duration of their illnesses, one hundred years later middling people might spend significant parts of their income on formal medical care. In the 1820s, the Lancashire cotton magnate Henry Ashworth was devoting between 1 and 3 per cent of his spending to doctors and druggist bills.[54] The Entwhistles of Bolton were spending about 8 per cent of their net income on drugs and doctors in the 1820s and 1830s, the Heywoods of Bolton up to 9 per cent of their income in some years and the Bolton attorney John Holden up to 7 per cent.[55] Families like the Heskeths in west Lancashire also spent considerable amounts on medicine and ingredients from the chemist H. Armstrong, though there is much less evidence of such expenditure amongst ordinary middling families in this area.[56] The medical marketplace, then, had certainly arrived by the early nineteenth century at the latest, and Figure 3.9 reproduces a bill sent to the Crompton family of Bolton for medical treatment in 1804.

The diary of Elizabeth Shackleton during her prolonged illness in the late 1770s and early 1780s can begin to show us how the medical marketplace manifested itself at individual level. She consulted four doctors. Her regular doctor was Thomas Turner from Colne but she also called out Dr Haworth of Clitheroe, Dr Midgely of Colne and Dr Hall of Manchester. They could do little to combat her multiple illnesses. Turner tried and retried his whole repertoire – physick (a mixture designed to produce vomiting), blistering (making blisters on the patient in the belief that it would draw out infection), taking blood, advising on

Figure 3.9: Bill for medical treatment addressed to the Crompton family Source: Item ZCR/17/1, 'Bill', reproduced by kind permission of Bolton Archive and Local Studies Unit.

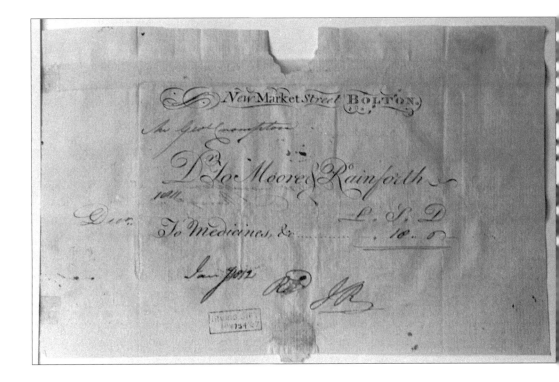

life-style and applying dressings – but hardly arrested her decline. Dr Haworth tried a different approach. Calling on the 14 February 1781 he 'examined my heel made light I thought of my illness, he called it the gout and . . . said he wo'd send me something that he was sure wo'd help me'. Thereafter he corresponded with Shackleton. On 5 March 'Mr Haworth sent julep, pills and cream of tartar . . . with proper directions how to use them'. On the 4 April he wrote again 'Received a letter and another bottle of rheumatism drops and a paper of bitters from Mr Haworth'. On 5 April,

> about noon Mr Howarth came to meet Mr Turner by appointment. As soon as they had talked a little they looked at my foot, which they both consulted and agreed most proper to be cut which Mr Turner did 2 ways. . . .[57]

These interventions failed too. Occasionally, families got involved and insisted on further medical opinions. On 19 May,

> When dear good valuable Mrs Parker looked at it [her foot] . . . my brother and her insisted I wo'd send for doctor Edward Hall it was agreed Mr Turner sho'd write to him this night to desire he wo'd come over here.

On 22 May,

> About 1 this morning I took laudanum which compos'd me that I did not get up till late came down at half past 12, before I sat down and without breakfast who sho'd I see but Doctor Edward Hall . . . We then began to talk of my disorder, he said it was the scurvy, beg'd I wo'd take a very slight vomit, then to take some med's he wo'd order. Whatever I did to keep my body open. He look'd at and dress'd my foot, he said he did not fear but it wo'd do well. The issue was come out but it was foul wanted cleansing the edges to be kept down scraped with an old knife or that they wo'd go callous. He wo'd order proper dressings and hop'd to put me in a good way. I was to drink porter or port wine no ale or small beer. To eat nothing salt, high season'd and but little butter.

Dr Hall's intervention also failed, and Elizabeth Shackleton's tolerance of this persistent failure provides evidence of how strong belief in doctors could become by the later eighteenth century. Figure 3.10, reproducing a letter written by Robert Heywood which seeks out medical expertise in Manchester, suggests that consulting a wide range of doctors was, in this area of the county at least, very common.

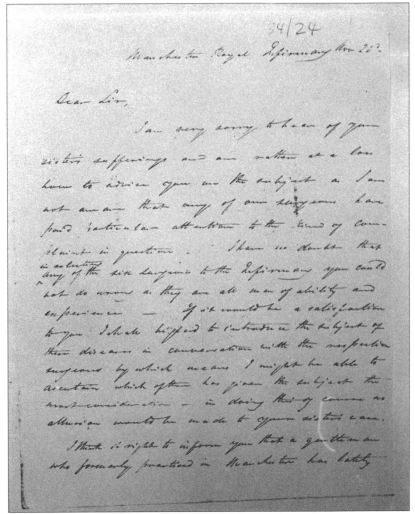

Figure 3.10: Robert Heywood's letter seeking doctors Source: Item ZHE/34/24, 'Letter', reproduced by kind permission of Bolton Archive and Local Studies Unit.

William St Clare's correspondence with Shackleton's relatives provides us with more details of the sorts of treatment being pursued by late eighteenth and early nineteenth century doctors, and of the nature of middling attitudes towards medical men. Thus, describing his medical response to fever in the young Thomas Parker in September 1790, St Clare wrote:

> He was instantly bled. I found his blood much inflamed. This seemed to produce good effect for the fever is not quite so brisk this morning. I have ordered a blister to be applied to the pained part of his left side, and such other remedies as I judged necessary . . .[58]

Writing to Mrs Whitacker in the advanced stages of her pregnancy in 1816 he advised:

a good deal of attention has to be paid to the bowels. I don't mean
however that it will be necessary to go beyond the measure of just
keeping them moderately open. This may be answered by occasionally
taking a neat spoonful of castor oil, or two or three aperient pills, as
prescribed on the other side, as may be found most agreeable . . .[59]

The prescription which followed, clearly meant to be made up by an
apothecary, consisted 'R extract colocynth c, aloes spic, sod. sub. carbon
(d), extract anthernid (d), ol. carni (d), mucilary qs vt ft mass and ri (d),
sign, capt (d) vit (d) hor somm, pro (rom)'. In short, there is some
support here for the idea that St Clare was part of a profession which,
through its use of language, was seeking to take control of the health of
middling people. Yet, as the text of the letter indicates, this was
happening but slowly even in the most medically vibrant part of the
county. St Clare was obliged to offer a simple alternative to his pills,
suggesting that middling patients retained control of their illnesses for
some considerable time.

Partial support for another of the generalisations of medical history
can also be found in this sort of narrative evidence. The tone of St Clare's
letters and the detail given in the Shackleton diary suggest that doctors
worked hard to put their mushrooming medical relationships with
patients on a sound social footing as well. This process might involve
social visiting and providing services over and above those medical to
middling families. Dr Haworth regularly carried messages on behalf of
Elizabeth Shackleton to the Parker family. Her regular doctor, Dr Turner,
was obliged to lend furniture and wine and throw dinner parties for the
Shackletons. And all of her doctors adopted a respectful tone in their
communications. William St Clare is an even better example of a doctor
wanting to encourage deeper social relations. He wrote in effusive terms
to Thomas Parker on 13 February 1780 to congratulate him on the birth
of a son,

> It is with unfeigned pleasure I congratulate you on the birth of your
> son . . . the young gentleman is a rare thumping lad and none of
> your half got things. I am Sir with great respect Your most obedient
> servant . . .[60]

By 1806 his family were not only on visiting terms but St Clare's
daughter was invited to stay at the Parker house for an extended period.[61]
St Clare had an even more cosy relationship with the Whitackers. His
son stayed with the Whitacker family at Simonstone in September 1816
and St Clare was godfather to one of their children.[62] He sent fish and
other produce, procured servants and acted as an estate agent. He took in
the Whitacker children, grandchildren and nephews and nieces when

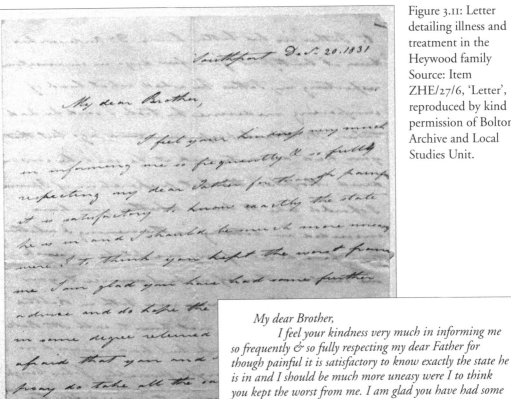

Figure 3.11: Letter detailing illness and treatment in the Heywood family Source: Item ZHE/27/6, 'Letter', reproduced by kind permission of Bolton Archive and Local Studies Unit.

> *My dear Brother,*
>   *I feel your kindness very much in informing me so frequently & so fully respecting my dear Father for though painful it is satisfactory to know exactly the state he is in and I should be much more uneasy were I to think you kept the worst from me. I am glad you have had some further advice and do hope the new medicine has in some degree relieved him ....do take all the care you can of yourself & get rest whenever you have an opportunity.........*

they were ill, and found lodgings for the Whitacker children when they travelled in west Lancashire.[63]

Yet, it would be wrong to overstate the degree to which the medical marketplace, and particularly the role of doctors, developed in Lancashire before the nineteenth century. As we saw at the start of this chapter, the supply of doctors was constrained for the entire period covered by this book. Doctors tended to have patients spread over a wide area, and they were frequently away from home. Correspondence between doctor and patient could help to equate supply and demand for medical services, but, as the diary of Elizabeth Shackleton shows, middling patients usually preferred home visits. This, and problems such as frequent illness among doctors themselves, strictly limited the number of patients that even a hard working doctor with a good horse could see in the course of a week or month. It is thus no surprise to see middling narratives littered with references to doctors being away from home when called, doctors not coming when called and doctors coming too late. Elizabeth Shackleton was disappointed by her doctors eleven times between 1779 and 1781, enough to try the patience of many customers in the medical marketplace. And when doctors did arrive, of course, there was little in their medical kitbag. Drs Hall, Turner and St Clare would hardly inspire confidence amongst modern consumers, and a particularly good example of the ineffectiveness of doctoring is provided by Figure 3.12. This represents the bill of Dr Edward Bolling of Bolton to the family of Nathaniel Mason, who, despite all of the medical attention, died under his care in June 1809. Small wonder we find Anne Digby suggesting that 'Well-informed Georgian consumers showed marked scepticism about the remedies proffered by the medical professional, so that in many cases the household retained sovereignty as the consumer of its own physician. It also continued to patronise the medical fringe'.[64]

Figure 3.12: The bill of Dr Bolling
Source: Item ZZ/23/3, 'Bill', reproduced by kind permission of Bolton Archive and Local Studies Unit.

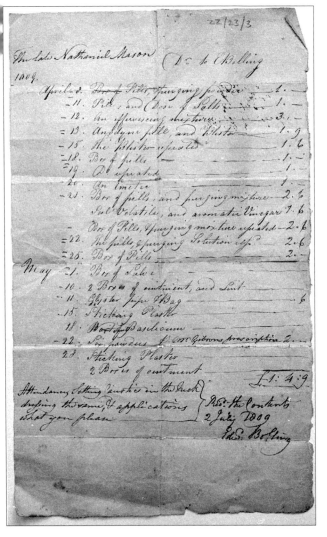

This observation provides the signpost to other important medical care strategies deployed by middling families in Lancashire. As they demanded more doctors and more medical opinions, so they also demanded more in the way of medical aid from irregulars and from quacks. Though Chamberlain suggests that the development of medicine as a commodity radically reduced the influence of irregulars, this was not the case in Lancashire.[65] We have already seen, for instance, that the Whitacker family had recourse to several medical professionals during the late eighteenth and early nineteenth centuries. They also turned to the local Simonstone irregular, David Robinson, blacksmith. In a remarkable list, Robinson noted the medicines delivered to the family by his daughter.[66] It consisted:

July 28	A small bottle of acid drops
July 31	A parcil of Strengthening powder
	A quart infusion of bark in wine
	A larger bottle of drops
August 5	Pill for the teeth and drawing tooth
September 9	Drops
September 10	Powders
	An astringent draught
September 13	Large opening mixture
September 17	A box of opening pills
	Powders
	Drops

William St Clare was clearly right to tread carefully in the strength of his advice to the family. In similar fashion, Roger Dewhurst, gentleman, and John Holden, attorney, actively supplemented the remedies proffered by Bolton doctors with those offered by local irregulars such as James Hide of Longworth and James Hargreaves of Deane.[67] And there is no doubt at all that middling families used quacks, a fact confirmed by the frequency with which flyers for patent remedies are preserved in family archives.

In turn, families who used quacks were also likely to be families with enduring interests in self-diagnosis and self-treatment. Elizabeth Shackleton mixed and took her own physick and purchased and administered laudanum. Her friends and family gave her recipes and medical advice and sometimes brought medicine when they visited her. She in turn passed on recipes and the prescriptions of her doctors to friends and family, facilitating the spread of knowledge that might be used to underpin self-dosing. Moreover, we should bear in mind that Shackleton was part of the group of Parker women who brewed their own medicine (to combat rabies) and offered it to the general public. As Amanda Vickery shows, well over 150 people came in person or sent their agents to buy the Parker remedy between 1767 and 1777.[68] That Shackleton was not alone in retaining an interest in self-dosing can be shown by a cursory analysis of the remarkable collection of middling 'commonplace books' to be found in Lancashire archives.[69] Collectively, these offer remedies for everything from mortal illness to small niggling complaints like toothache and colds. Figure 3.13 reproduces a remedy for a cough drawn from such commonplace books.

Francis Barton of Kirkham provides an early example. His recipes were short and simple. For gallstones he recommended 'one and a half pounds of red onions, 2 garlick, one pint of Holland gin. Put the gin into the above

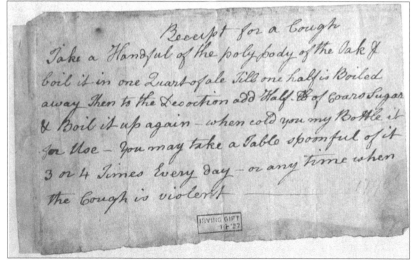

articles and let it stand for 12 hours and take the whole at seven different times in the morning, fasting'. For whooping cough 'Take a handful of house leek, quarter of brown sugar and boil them together until . . . the consistency of a syrup, the house leek to be squeezed and the juice to be mixed with the syrup'.[70] The lack of herbal remedies here is interesting, but unfortunately we do not have sufficient number of other early examples to draw concrete conclusions about the sophistication of early eighteenth century self-dosing. By the 1760s and 1770s there certainly was much more in the way of herbal components to recipes. A Hawkshead merchant in 1763 advised:

> For the scurvy that you so much complain off, and mingles with your gout, and perhaps envenerates it, the most parable medicine, and which everybody takes here, is the decoction of Burdock root, made very strong and drank in large quantities, a quart at least in a day . . . it may not be amiss to contrive some exercise, even to perspiration, after your decoction.[71]

By 1772, the Dickonson family were celebrating the value of balsam and giving recipes for several different types. Their commonplace book claimed that when using basalmic tinctures:

> There is no cut of iron if not mortal but it heals in eight days time, for the gout and is a sovereign medicine anointing the part effected for the toothache, a perfect cure apl'd with a bit of cotton, it cures all ulcers, cancer or canker, it cures the bites or stings of all venomous beasts and especially mad dogs, it cures the enerods and piles, anointing them when you go to bed and it is found for all swellings, corruptions and fistules . . .[72]

Of course, such universal claims are reminiscent of the nineteenth century quack, but it is important to realise that accompanying recipes such as 'Mrs Pansfford's Fryers balsam' did have a strong herbal connection. The latter recipe used the herbs Benjamin, Angelica and St John's Wort mixed in alcohol, and must have had very strong antiseptic properties. Moreover, the recipe used a whole host of foreign ingredients, suggesting that middling people had access to a ready supply of basic ingredients. The Dickonson recipe for headache confirms the value of the recipe book, suggesting that:

> take one ounce of zestory cinnamon, cloves, mace and nutmegs of each 6 drams, ginger and long pepper of each 2 drams, flowers of camomile half an ounce, saffron 2 drams, spinkard 1 dram, all gross bruised and tied in a fine cloth rag which is put into a glass vessel and put upon it the best canary wine 2 quarts and let is stand infusing for the space of 10 days, strain it off for use.

What is most interesting about the Dickonsons, however, is that they assume several recipes are so well known that the process of making them is not spelled out. Both Jesuit's Powder and Sir Walter Raleigh's Cordial fall into this category. Such assumptions speak volumes for a rich late eighteenth century culture of self-dosing in Lancashire.

By the early nineteenth century, the Marshall family commonplace book suggests that middling families around Wigan had begun to use some of the core ingredients of the emergent chemists and quacks. For colic and stomach upset, they recommended:

> Magnesia alloe (a dram and a half), rhubarb powder (a dram), ginger powder (a dram), cordial confection (6 drams), oil of aniseed (3 drops) syrup of saffron, as much as will make it into an electuary, twice or thrice a day.[73]

while strains could be alleviated with a lineament of '1 oz of vitriol, 2oz of spirit wine, 6oz of turps and 1 dram of origanum'. These recipes and others in the book have a traceable medical value, and are characteristic of the increasing sophistication of recipes in the later commonplace books. William Heyns' book, assembled up to 1840, provides a particularly good example of this tendency. Covering remedies or treatments for problems ranging from the menopause and skin inflammations to persistent fever, the book is precise in its measuring of ingredients and its dosing, and notably picks up on the nineteenth century trend to prefer medicine in pill form. For fever, Heyns had a recipe which involved 'Sulphur of quinine (24 grams), turkey rhubarb (24 grams), Jamaican ginger (12 grams), mix into 24 pills, take 1 night and morning'. For consumption and general strengthening he suggested 'Take extract of bark 1 dram, extract of gentium 1 dram, myrrh 1 dram, sulphate of iron half a dram, syrup of ginger to form the mass and made into 60 pills'.[74]

We could continue with the quotation of recipes from the Lancashire commonplace books. The key point, however, is what lessons for middling attitudes towards health, doctors and the medical marketplace we should draw from the very existence and survival of commonplace books. On the one hand, there is reason to be sceptical that they can tell us anything, as was suggested in the case of Benjamin Shaw above. Commonplace books might represent no more than simply idle collecting, placing, as they often do, recipes for medicine alongside personal memoranda, records of family events and food recipes.[75] They were not, in other words, meant to be used. And whether they were meant to be used or not, it is often difficult to date the contents of the commonplace book with any certainty, to fathom the provenance of the recipes or to establish their medical value. Such observations have led Joan Lane to doubt whether we can draw any very revealing conclusions about the medical lives of middling people from their commonplace books.[76] Yet on the other hand, in a rich collection of commonplace books such as we see in Lancashire, it is possible to trace developments in the sophistication of remedies and ingredients (particularly starting to incorporate non-native herbs) over time, and also some increase in the likely medical benefit of the remedies noted. And recipes were used and valued, as I have attempted to show elsewhere.[77] Indeed, for families in west Lancashire, with relatively few doctors to cover a relatively wide area and rich cultural traditions of avoiding medical professionals, it is conceivable that the commonplace book was a mainstay of medical care outside of mortal illness. The very fact that these sources survive is probably testimony to the value placed upon them both as family documents and useful source of information. Chamberlain's conclusion that 'compared to the state of medical science at the time, many of the traditional remedies . . . were soundly based and reasonably efficacious. The new herbalism had a strong anti-doctor bias.' perhaps deserves more attention in the Lancashire context.[78]

4. *Conclusion*

Clearly, responses to middling ill-health were diverse. For some families such as the Whitackers and the Shackletons, the medical professional played a pivotal role and may have been the first port of call even in cases of relatively minor illness. However, there is preliminary evidence that doctors played much less of a role and that middling families were reticent about engaging with the medical marketplace. For these people, and more generally in the sense of the enduring importance of self-dosing, responses to ill-health involved as much continuity as change in the eighteenth and nineteenth centuries. Similar conclusions might be drawn about the responses of the poor.

A brief analysis of the account book of Dr Loxham of Poulton confirms that we must tread warily when talking about the spread of doctoring under the auspices of the expanding medical marketplace.[79] The accounts, stretching from the 1750s to the 1780s, detail the treatment records of between 740 and 780 patients (there are 40 cases where entries in different parts of the book may refer to the same person or family). Figure 3.14 shows the occupational distribution of the patients. When we also include the 63 people who were given status ascriptions rather than trades, it is clear that Loxham treated people across the social spectrum. He certainly engaged with some of the most important Fylde families, including the Hornbys, Lackerbys and Cliftons. And his medical connections with some patients were very strong indeed. Figure 3.15 reproduces the account for Richard Lackerby which shows that Loxham was a relatively frequent visitor and that he charged for advice and visits as much as he charged for the medicine. This is precisely what the literature on professionalization and the medical marketplace predicts.

However, what is most noticeable about the Loxham account book is how *infrequently* both his middling and labouring poor patients called on his services compared to the scale of ill-health outlined in chapter two. On average he saw each of his 740 patients just under once every three years, and considerably less than this where we ignore midwifery cases.

Figure 3.14: The occupations of the patients of Dr Loxham Source: Drawn from document DDPr 25/6, 'Account Book of Dr Loxham' at the Lancashire Record Office, Preston.

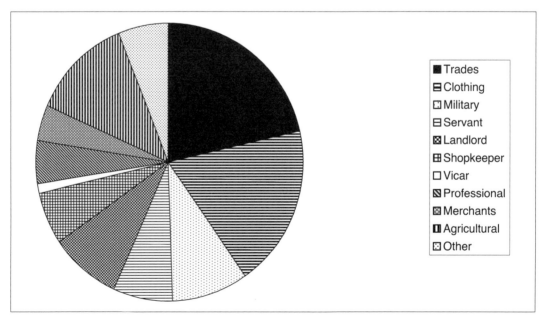

Legend:
- ■ Trades
- ⊟ Clothing
- ▯ Military
- ⊟ Servant
- ⊠ Landlord
- ⊞ Shopkeeper
- ▢ Vicar
- ⊠ Professional
- ⊠ Merchants
- ▮ Agricultural
- ⊡ Other

Map 2: Dr Loxham's
circuit. Map drawn
by Chris Beacock.

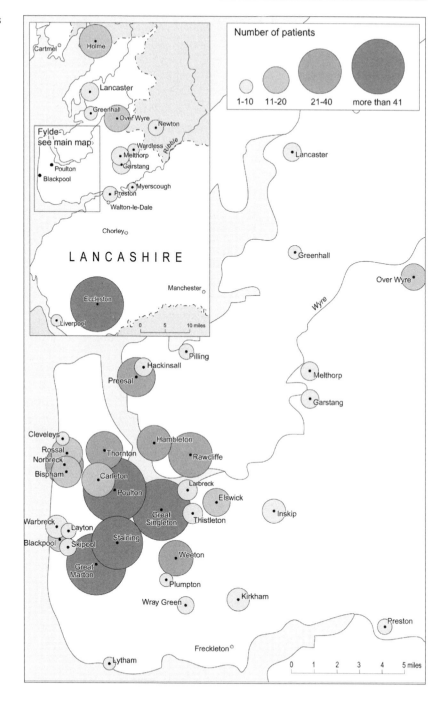

Date	Description	£	s	d
1 mar 1760	Rich'd Lackerby Esqr at Eccleston			
	to a call upon Mrs Lackerby		5	0
2	a visit to her		10	6
	to haust anodyn			
10	a visit to her coming from Elswick		10	6
16 may	a visit to Mrs Lackerby		10	6
	to julep cum tinct cart sal diuret [d]		2	0
	to bol a sperm cart pul feb nitro [d]		1	0
18	a visit to Mrs Lackerby			
	to boluses repeated & julep [d]		3	0
20	a visit to Mrs Lackerby			
	bol [d] repeated & julep salin [d]		3	0
22	a visit to Mr Lackerby			
	to julep cum cart [d] bol repet'd [d]		2	0
24	a visit to Mrs Lackerby			
	julep repeated		1	6
26	to do [d] & bol [d]		3	0
27	a visit			
29	do			
	too julep [d] & bol [d]		3	0
31	a visit to do			
	to mist salin [d] syr diacod [d]		2	6
	to spt ND & hard perlat [d]		1	0
2 jun	a visit to do & hard perlat [d]			
	to mist salin [d] }		2	0
3	to hard perlat [d] & syr a mecon		1	0
	medicines	1	4	0
	(vide 133)			
4 jun 1760	Rich' Lackenby Esqr of Eccleston			
	a visit to Mrs Lackenby			
	ti julep salin [d]		2	0
	a visit to Mrs Leckerby			
	to bol sperm cati cum trigu [d]		1	0
	to syr mercuric [d] & hard pertal [d]		1	0
	a visit to master Leckenby			
12	a 2d do to do			
	a 3d visit to mast'r Leckerby			
9	a 4th visit to do			
10	to julep cum sal diuret [d] for Mrs		2	0
	to elix purgoric [d]		1	0
	a 5th visit to mast'e Leckerby			
	to 4 boluses repeated for Mrs Leckerby			6
12	a 6th visit to mast'e Leckerby			
13	a 7th do & spt ND (2)			6
	to syr e mercuri [d]		1	0

Figure 3.15: The medical accounts of Richard Lackerby
Source: Drawn from document DDPr 25/6, 'Account Book of Dr Loxham' at the Lancashire Record Office, Preston.

14	to solutis sperm cati [d] for mast'r	1	0
	an 8th visit		
15	a 9th do		
16	a 10th visit		
17	a visit to Mrs Leckerby		
	too soltia sperm cati [d]	2	0
	to syn e mercuri		
18	a visit to Mrs Leckerby		
19	a visit to do		
	to solut sperm cati & c [d]	1	6
20	to do	1	6
	a visit		
21	another visit		
22	a visit & syr mercotic		6
23	a visit		
24	do & hard perlat [d]		6
	to mist salin [d] cum sar russic	2	0
	to dos testac [d]	1	0
	to pol columb in chard		6
25	to 2 visits		
26	a visit		
27	do & pul columb [d] in chart [d]		6
	to athiops miomer dos [d]		
	to upl rhei [d] } for master	1	6
20	a visit to Mrs Leckerby		
29	do do		
30	do		
31	do		
1 jul	to dos testac [d]	1	6
2	do		
	to dix lintiv [d]		6
3	a visit		
4	do		
5	do		
6	do		
8	do		
	to dos testac [d]		6
10	do		
12	do		
14	do		
	to elect pectoral		
17	to linct pectoral		
18	a visit		
do	do		
	medicines	2 17	6
	(Vide 144)		

How to interpret these observations is problematic. There is a proverbial chicken and egg situation here. Loxham had several hundred patients and so could have devoted little time to them over a year even had they demanded, but he may have had to generate that number of patients given low demand for his medical services. Certainly, part of the reason for his limited contact with most patients may have been the scale of his doctoring circuit. Map 2 shows the relationship between Poulton and the places of residence of his patients. We can see that he travelled widely, which would have cut down the number of patients he could see. The number of times he was turned back in mid-journey could not have helped in this respect. But perhaps also we see the lessons of this chapter coming through. Some of his patients would have engaged multiple medical men, others might have actively sought to limit their connections with doctors, and even more would have turned to quackery or continued their traditional self-dosing. However we interpret these charts, it cannot be denied that much of the ill-health life of middling and labouring people continued to be experienced outside formal doctoring arrangements and probably outside the medical marketplace as well. The need to look carefully at enduring regional patterns of response to ill-health on their own terms is thus clear. What is also clear is that the economics of doctoring were likely to have been as complex as the responses of patients. It is this theme that we take up in the next chapter.

Notes

1. See S. A.King, *Poverty and Welfare 1700–1850: A Regional Perspective* (Manchester University Press, 2000).

2. S. A. King and A. Weaver, 'Lives in many hands: The medical landscape in Lancashire 1700–1820', *Medical History*, 45 (2000), 173–200.

3. J. Lane, '"The doctor scolds me": the diaries and correspondence of patients in eighteenth century England', in Porter (ed.), *Patients and Practitioners* (Cambridge University Press, 1985), 205–48, pp. 217.

4. Lancashire Record Office (hereafter LRO) PR 1605, 'Alston accounts' and LRO DDX 1/6, 'Bispham with Norbreck vestry minutes'.

5. Chorley Public Library, 'Minute book, 1800–1818'.

6. LRO DDX 28/78, 'Accounts of the overseer of Clitheroe'.

7. LRO PR 2918 3/3, 'Tatham Fell Account Book'.

8. LRO PR 2995 1/25, 'Ledger'.

9. LRO PR 2956 3/1, 'Annual accounts'.

10. Bolton Local Studies Library (hereafter BL) ZWL 36, 'Longworth overseer accounts'.

11. LRO PR 2918/3/3, 'Tatham Fell Account Book'.

12. LRO PR 1603, 'Overseer accounts of Alston'.

13. LRO DDX 1/6, 'Bispham with Norbreck vestry minutes'.

14. LRO PR 2995 1/25, 'Poor law accounts of Easington'.

15. BL ZZ 238 1/130/6, 'Agreement'.

16. LRO DDX 28/257, 'Langshaw collection' and LRO DDX 386/3, 'Garstang vestry minutes'.

17. See BL ZWL 36, 'Longworth overseer accounts'. Also J. V. Pickstone, *Health, Disease and Medicine in Lancashire, 1750–1950* (UMIST Occasional Paper, 1981) and J. V. Pickstone, *Medicine and Industrial Society: A History of Hospital Development in Manchester and its Region, 1752–1946* (Manchester University Press, 1985).

18. The Liverpool dispensary records are located in the Sydney Jones Library, University of Liverpool. See also I.Loudon, 'The origins and growth of the dispensary movement in England', *Bulletin of the History of Medicine*, 55 (1981), 322–42.

19. LRO DDPd Accession 4125, 'Preston dispensary Mss'.

20. BL ZZ 238 1/130/7, 'List'.

21. LRO DDPd Accession 4125, 'Preston dispensary Mss'.

22. LRO DDBa 1 and 2, 'Account book of gifts to the poor', DDBa 3, 'Account book of cloth given to the poor' and DDBa 16, 'Account book including gifts to the poor'.

23. BL ZBD 3/16, 'List of subscribers'.

24. LRO DDX 2098 1/2, 'Sick society payments'. See also LRO PR 2994, 'Sick society books' and LRO DDX 150, 'Sick society of Clitheroe'.

25. See F. M. M. Eden, *Observations on friendly societies* (Black, 1801) and M. Gray, *The History of Bury Lancashire from 1660 to 1876* (Bury Times, 1970), 79–80.

26. For a particularly good selection, see BL PGB 2/1–76, 'Friedly society certificates 1799–1834'.

27. M. Gorsky, 'The growth and distribution of English friendly societies in the early nineteenth century', *Economic History Review*, 51 (1998), 489–511.

28. R. J. Fitton (ed.), *The Family Economy of the Working Classes in the Cotton Industry (1784–1833)*, (Chetham Society, 1965).

29. M. Chamberlain, *Old Wives Tales: Their History, Remedies and Spells* (Virago, 1981), 88.

30. A. Secord, 'Science in the pub: artisan botanists in early nineteenth century Lancashire', *History of Science*, 32 (1994), 269–315.

31. A. Crosby (ed), *The Family Records of Benjamin Shaw, Mechanic of Dent, Dolphinholme and Preston, 1772–1841* (Chetham Society, 1991), lv, and J. L. West, *The Taylors of Lancashire: Bonesetters and Doctors, 1750–1890* (Townson, 1977).

32. LRO PR 2918 3/3, 'Tatham Fell account books'.

33. J. Fern, *Observations on Manchester and its Region* (Privately published, 1839).

34. For the standard work on quacks, see R.Porter, *Health for Sale: Quackery in England 1660–1850* (Manchester University Press, 1989) and R. Porter, *Quacks: Fakers and Charlatans in English Medicine* (Tempus, 2000). Also I. Loudon, 'The vile race of quacks with which this country is infested', in Bynum and Porter, *Medical Fringe*, 106–28 and E. Bosdin-Leech, *Early Medicine and Quackery in Lancashire* (Ranold Press, 1938). The term 'quack' masks a variety of practitioners, but for our purposes, it is important to distinguish between the quacks who brewed their own (often opiate based) 'medicines' and the 'quack middleman' who sold such remedies after purchasing them wholesale.

35. BL ZZ/238 1 Page 175, 'Flyer'.

36. LRO DDHu 53/62/266, 'Quack bill'. My italics.

37. LRO DDX 12/10/1, 'Grocer's account book' and the quack advertisements culled

from newspapers by W. Durham, *Chronological Notes on the History of the Town and Parish of Blackburn* (THCL Books, 1988).

38. BL ZZ 357, 'Physick in Bolton, 1779'.

39. LRO DDHu 53 82/279, 'Flyer'.

40. For a particulary good example of the cheapness of these books see the <u>new</u> copy of *Armstrong's Art of Preserving Health*, purchased by Richard Hodgkinson for 6d. in 1795. F. Wood and K. Wood (eds.), *A Lancashire Gentleman: The Letters and Journals of Richard Hodgkinson 1763–1847* (Alan Sutton, 1992), 98.

41. For instance, leaflets, circulating in most central Lancashire towns during the 1830s offered instruction on 'How to avoid Cholera, Being plain directions for poor people'. See BL ZWL 73/26, 'Leaflet'. Also W. H. Clerke, *Thoughts on the Means of Preserving the Health of the Poor by Prevention and Suppression of Epidemic Fevers. Addressed to the Inhabitants of the Town of Manchester and Several Populous Trading Places Surrounding and Connected with it* (Black, 1790).

42. LRO DDX 1554/10, 'Receits of various sorts'. The book *Doctors Syntax* was available to buy in 1799 and may have been necessary with some of these recipes.

43. His alternative cure for jaundice was 'Take the roots of dog grass and boil them in old ale, a quart, and strain and drink a gill every morning'.

44. LRO DDX 1554/5, 'Catalogue of trees' and LRO DDX 1554/5, 'List of herbs'.

45. See J. Gillow and A. Hewitson (eds), *The Tyldesley Diary: Personal Record of Thomas Tyldesley* (Privately Published, 1873). For context, see A. Wear, 'Puritan perceptions of illness in seventeenth century England', in Porter, *Patients*, 55–99.

46. For a discussion of this point in the light of a seventeenth century Essex family, see L. M. Beier, 'In sickness and in health: A seventeenth century family's experience', in Porter, *Patients*, 101–28.

47. W. Brockbank and F. Kenworthy, *The Diary of Richard Kay, a Lancashire Doctor* (Chetham Society, 1968).

48. King and Weaver, 'Lives'.

49. LRO DDb 81/39, 'Diary'.

50. LRO DDb 72/495–497, 'Leters'.

51. LRO DDWh 4/101, 'Letter'.

52. LRO DDWh 4/105, 'Letter'.

53. See Wilkinson, *The Letters*.

54. BL ZWL 69, 'Personal accounts'.

55. BL ZZ 530/1–3, 'Diaries and memorandum books'; BL ZZ 486 (additional), 'Entwhistle collection'; BL ZHE, 'Heywood diaries'.

56. DDHe 62/114, 'Account of medicines from chemist H. Armstrong for Sir T. G. Hesketh Bart'.

57. DDb 81/39, 'Diary'.

58. LRO DDb 72/495, 'Letter'.

59. LRO DDWh 4/92, 'Letter'.

60. LRO DDb 72/492, 'Letter'.

61. LRO DDb 72/500, 'Letter'.

62. LRO DDWh 4/87, 'Letter'.

63. LRO DDb 72/502, 'Letter'.

64. Digby, *Making*, 42.

65. Chamberlain, *Old Wives*.

66. Humanities Research Centre Archive, Oxford Brookes University.

67. BL ZZ 387, 'Dewhurst papers' and BL ZZ 530/1–3, 'Diaries and memoranda of John Holden'.

68. A. Vickery, *The Gentleman's Daughter: women's lives in Georgian England* (Yale University Press, 1998), appendix 6. For enduring concern over rabies, see the cure offered in Manchester Central Library, *Manchester Magazine, 11th August, 1741*.

69. Commonplace books usually contain recipes for medical remedies mixed up with recipes for food, sayings and memoranda. They were family documents and were usually periodically updated. More widely, middling collections are littered with letters offering advice and individual remedies for everyday complaints. See LRO DDCa 17/234, 'A cure for Thrush'; LRO DDGr M 1/6, 'Receit for bilious habits'; and LRO DDSc 127/217, 'Recipe for red powder'.

70. LRO DDX 151/2, 'Book of disbursements, 1728'.

71. Cumbria Record Office WDX 460, 'Letter'.

72. LRO DDX 274/2, 'Recipe book'. See also the diaries in this collection for usage and ill-health context.

73. Wigan Record Office D/D 2 EHC volume 54, 'Recipes'.

74. LRO DDX 235/1, 'William Heyns, his book of 1840'.

75. For good examples see LRO RCHy 81/1/63, 'Recipes' and LRO DDX 576/2, 'The diary of Edward Cooke of Preston'.

76. J. Lane, 'The doctor', in Porter, *Patients*, 241.

77. King and Weaver, 'Lives'.

78. Chamberlain, *Old Wives*, 95.

79. LRO DDPr25/6, 'Account book'.

CHAPTER FOUR

The economics of doctoring

1. *Overview*

The last chapter outlined the efforts made by doctors to encourage social and medical connections between themselves and middling families. At the other end of the spectrum, it showed doctors contracted to the poor law. We must be clear that most of this poor law work was ill-paid, especially where agreements were to include provision of medicines.[1] In Aughton, the doctors treating the poor in the 1770s were contracted at just £2 2s. per annum including medicines. In Ulnes Walton the figure was £2 and in Clitheroe £2 5s. 6d., to include all eventualities except childbirth and smallpox. The doctors for Caton Gilbert Union were better paid, but generally poor law authorities north of the Ribble were reluctant to pay even the restricted fees offered by their contemporaries in south Lancashire.[2] Thus, in Newton-with-Scales the average poor law contract between 1753 and 1834 was worth just £2 to doctors, while in Kirkham between 1804 and 1819 Dr Parkinson was paid between £1 and £3 for his services.[3] Medical historians are split on how we should regard the engagement of doctors with the poor law under these terms – were they doing loss-making work to stop somebody else getting a foothold in the local medical marketplace and to enhance their status by doing what was essentially charitable work? Or should we regard doctoring the poor as evidence of a profession under economic pressure? Answering this question, and more widely uncovering the economic position of doctors, is beset with problems of source and interpretation. Account books for doctors outside the biggest urban areas have rarely survived.[4] Letters and bills survive in greater number in family and poor law archives, but they are in themselves problematic. As we will go on to see, issuing a bill was no guarantee of payment and even where the recipient of the bill was inclined to pay it, they often did not do so on time. Moreover, Lancastrian patients seem to have regarded a bill as the basis for haggling. The biggest interpretive problem, however, is the nature of the professional life-cycle. It is clear that some doctors specialised in a specific segment of the market – poor, middling or aristocratic – throughout their careers. Others consistently treated people across the social spectrum. Still more specialised in different groups of people at different points of their professional life-cycle. It is thus difficult to reconstruct a 'representative' economic situation for doctors.[5]

This has not stopped some historians trying. Anne Digby and Irvine Loudon have been at the forefront of disentangling the economics of doctoring on the national stage.[6] From their work we might draw several important conclusions which can frame this analysis of the situation in Lancashire. *First*, that the supply of doctoring services changed markedly over time. While there was always differing access to doctors between rural and urban areas (with doctors much more common in the latter than the former), between classes (with middling and aristocratic people able to call on the full range of medical men rather than just the surgeon-apothecary who was the mainstay of medical care for tradespeople) and between areas, much of the eighteenth century constituted a 'Golden Age' for medical practitioners. From the early nineteenth century the situation was reversed and competition amongst medical men became severe as the supply of fully and partly trained medical *men* overtook the growth rate of the general population.[7] *Second*, as the last chapter showed, neither in the eighteenth nor the nineteenth centuries were *regular* medical men successful in eliminating the competition of irregular practitioners, quacks and self-dosing. A *third* observation follows from this – that medicine could be a financially uncertain occupation which, while it could yield fortunes for some could also leave many on the very edge of gentility and others bankrupt. Exact earning figures are hard to come by for the period covered by this book, but an average eighteenth century income for a well established surgeon-apothecary may have been of the order of £400. With increasing competition after 1800, incomes fell such that a rural surgeon might earn £250 and an urban practitioner only double this sum at best. This despite increased middling expenditure on medicine over time.[8] These were very poor rewards compared to other professions.[9] *Fourthly*, the most successful provincial medics were those who could judge potential demand for their services at different fee levels and set their charges accordingly, who were flexible in the face of changing market opportunities and who most quickly diversified into offering services rather than drugs. However, a *fifth* conclusion is that physicians and surgeons were more certain of making a respectable medical living (at least by the mid-point of their careers) than were the surgeon-apothecaries who were the forerunners of the modern General Practitioner. *Finally*, both Digby and Loudon observe that patients usually held the upper hand in economic relationships with their doctors given the adverse effect on a medical reputation of going to law in order to realise outstanding debts.

These are important general conclusions. What is much less well explored in medical historiography are the regional peculiarities of the economics of doctoring. Lancashire provides a rich array of until now under-used sources – poor law accounts, letters, deeds, a rare doctor's account book and other records – with which to put some regional flesh on these stark bones. The remainder of this chapter thus deals with the economics of doctoring, focusing mainly on the surgeon-apothecary.

2. Making a medical living in Lancashire

That some medical men made a healthy living from medicine in the county is not to be denied. Samuel Barton, surgeon to the Manchester Eye Hospital, became a member of the Royal College of Surgeons in 1811 and a fellow in 1844. His will directed property worth upwards of £20,000. Barton's apprentice, Samuel Crompton from Over Darwen, was likewise successful, becoming a member of the Royal College of Surgeons in 1839.[10] Edmund Lyon took longer to make his fortune, but nonetheless finished rather well.[11] So did Dr Marshall of Southport, and Figure 4.1 reproduces a complimentary letter about him.

Richard Kay of Baldingstone learnt the doctoring trade from his father and took over his patients later in life. While his diary, covering the first half of the eighteenth century, does not give us much in the way of figures, Kay lead a vigorous social life and appears to have had a diversified earning stream, including farming. To all intents and purposes, then, he was making a respectable living from his trade.[12] Doctors such as Charles White and William Blake published extensively and achieved national prominence.[13] As the last chapter implied, less well-known doctors like William St. Clare could also make a good living from middling patients. His first appearance in the Lancashire sources is in April 1778 when he appeared as a witness in a trial at Lancaster Castle, for a murder allegedly committed in Clitheroe in 1773. Figure 4.2 reproduces a page of the trial document. St Clare testified that he had been born in Nottingham and had taken over the patient list of Dr Moorhouse from Clitheroe who had died sometime before 1773. In April 1776 St. Clare was asked to examine a partially decomposed body that had appeared in the local

Figure 4.1: Letter complimenting Dr Marshall
Source: Item ZHE/41/10, 'Letter', reproduced by kind permission of Bolton Archive and Local Studies Unit.

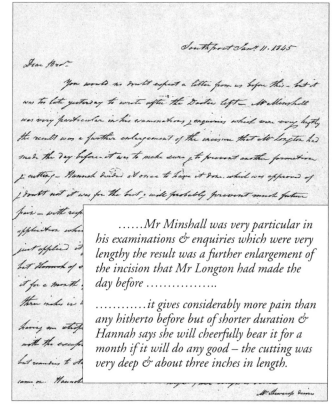

......Mr Minshall was very particular in his examinations & enquiries which were very lengthy the result was a further enlargement of the incision that Mr Longton had made the day before ....

............it gives considerably more pain than any hitherto before but of shorter duration & Hannah says she will cheerfully bear it for a month if it will do any good – the cutting was very deep & about three inches in length.

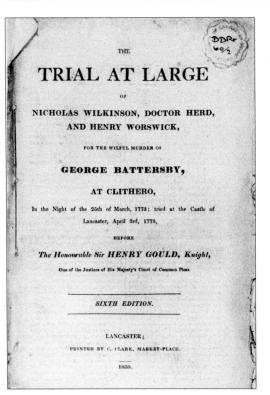

THE

TRIAL AT LARGE

OF

NICHOLAS WILKINSON, DOCTOR HERD,
AND HENRY WORSWICK,

FOR THE WILFUL MURDER OF

GEORGE BATTERSBY,

AT CLITHERO,

In the Night of the 26th of March, 1773; tried at the Castle of
Lancaster, April 3rd, 1778,

BEFORE

The Honourable Sir HENRY GOULD, Knight,

One of the Justices of His Majesty's Court of Common Pleas.

SIXTH EDITION.

LANCASTER;

PRINTED BY C. CLARK, MARKET-PLACE.

1830.

Figure 4.2: Trial at large, 1778 Source: Drawn from document DDPr 60/2, 'Trial at Large' at the Lancashire Record Office, Preston and reproduced by kind permission of the Lancashire Evening Post.

bone house. He testified that the body had been cut up after death and stored in quick lime for some time. He also testified that he had treated one of the defendants for a thumb strain on the day after the murder was supposed to have taken place. By the 1790s, as we have seen, St. Clare was doctor to the Parker family and by the early nineteenth century he combined his private practice with various public roles, including service as a paid consultant to the Preston infirmary and advisor to the Bolton infirmary.[14] Irregular practitioners and quacks could also make a comfortable living from the medical trade.[15]

Yet, notwithstanding the success of people like these, some doctors found it difficult to make a consistently acceptable living. We should expect no less given the general discussion of Digby and Loudon, but it is important to realise the sheer scale of uneconomic doctoring in the county and to draw out a few of its human faces. The story of Benjamin Wraith of Bolton, Chemist, druggist and Doctor is by no means unusual. Trained in Manchester, he came to Bolton in 1780, leasing a shop and house in Deansgate from the Trustees of Mary Crompton. By 1796 his income had expanded sufficiently for him to think about diversifying. He leased land next to his premises from Stephen Heels, a Butcher, for £61 per annum on a lease of 999 years, clearly intending to build on this prominent street corner. However, Wraith got into a costly right of way dispute at the same time as his income from doctoring fell away. In June 1798 he sought a mortgage on his land, but this was insufficient to prevent him sliding into bankruptcy at the age of 43 in July 1802.[16] He was not alone in this sad experience, nor in facing straightened economic circumstances. Dr James Scowcroft of Bolton Deansgate was forced to give up his lease after just one year in 1842. He tried again in 1845 but could afford to keep up his lease for only four years. He was declared bankrupt in 1846.[17] Dr Francis Carter of Poulton was sold up in June 1787 owing £31 10s. to direct creditors and 14s. 7d. in taxes. Figure 4.3 is a reproduction of the debt figures at the time of bankruptcy. This was a small debt to cause such misery and demonstrates the precarious situation that some doctors at the start of their careers in particular might find themselves forced to endure.[18]

Meanwhile, those who avoided bankruptcy might nonetheless experience considerable cash flow problems. As we will see in the next

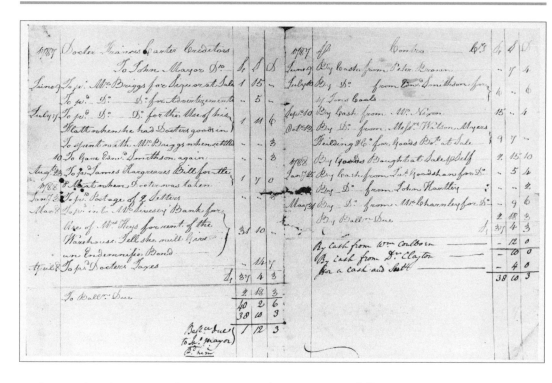

Figure 4.3: Debt schedule for Dr Carter of Poulton Source: Drawn from document DDPr 17/11, 'Accounts' at the Lancashire Record Office, Preston and reproduced by kind permission of the Lancashire Evening Post.

section, paying doctors on time was a rare phenomenon and for young doctors attempting to establish their own patient list from scratch cash flow problems could be fatal. This conclusion is familiar from the work of Digby and Loudon, but much of the evidence of payment terms and amounts comes from the late nineteenth century. Analysis of eighteenth century account books suggests, as we will see below, that even in the so-called 'Golden Age' of doctoring, cash flow could be a fundamental problem. Middling narratives also provide evidence on this issue. Elizabeth Shackleton of Alkincoats was eager to pay her practitioners. After a visit from Dr Hall on 21 May 1781, she wrote, 'Doctor Hall to go home with Mr Hartley to Broadley and sleep there and for me to send Mr Shackleton there tomorrow morning by 7 o'clock, or if Mr Shackleton wo'd not go for to send his fee by Richard'.[19] Then,

> Mr S went by 6 to Broadley where he found Doctor Hall, he breakfasted with him. The Doctor told him he did not apprehend danger in my foot he hop'd it would heal sound and do well. My disorder he took to be the scurvy, the gout and rheumatism mix'd. He told Mr S how my foot sho'd be dressed and what medicines he had order'd for me to take inwardly. Mr S gave Doctor Hall 4 guineas for coming over to me. *Mr S did not think he seem'd pleas'd with the fee*, said before they parted he wo'd be glad to hear under my own hand how I went on.[20]

Clearly, Doctor Hall's fee structure meant little to Mr Shackleton, whatever the attitude of his wife. More widely of course, the problems that doctors encountered in getting paid reflected both their weakness in relation to middling patients and (and perhaps most importantly) the simple fact that many doctors were not business people. Digby points out that there was nothing within the standard medical education that taught doctors how to be good business people. Even if there had been many doctors would have struggled to put theory into practice. Evidence from the account books of patients suggests persuasively that as late as the 1810s Lancashire doctors had simply failed to build in allowances for late payment to charges levied on middling families.[21] As late as the twentieth century, Digby reminds us, some of the highest levels of unpaid fees (coming to light when practices were sold or partners advertised for) in the entire country were to be found in Lancashire.[22] If doctors were economically successful in Lancashire, we might surmise that this was success by accident rather than planning.

However, irregular payment and consequent cash flow problems was not what lay at the heart of the fragile medical livings to be made by some Lancashire doctors. They faced several other problems, and it is worth spending some time looking at the framework within which doctors played out their professional and economic lives. Thus one of the *most pressing* problems for Lancashire doctors, as the last chapter demonstrated, was that medical pluralism remained a force to be reckoned with until well into the nineteenth century. Even more than in the rest of the country, middling and other patients seem to have retained their belief that it was best to explore as many medical avenues as possible in response to illness. In particular, the quack remedy and self-dosing took money out of the pockets of doctors. A *second* problem for Lancashire doctors seeking to make a viable living was that there were enduring pockets of imbalance in supply of, and demand for, doctor services. The idea that in some places there were simply too many doctors might at first blush seem difficult to reconcile with Anne Digby's characterisation of the county as poorly doctored, and with the more general notion that intense competition amongst regular medical men was mainly a nineteenth century phenomenon. On the face of it too, notions of oversupply are equally hard to reconcile with one of the basic theoretical premises of medical history – that the medical marketplace was an example of what economists call perfect equilibrium. Crudely, when there were too many doctors, some would leave and when there were not enough, doctors would arrive, until everyone was making a comfortable living. However, a number of peculiarities of the Lancashire medical marketplace mean that reconciling these ideas is not as hard as it appears. Elsewhere I have suggested, for instance, that there was a distinct regionality to medicine in Lancashire – broadly the west of the county turned less to doctors than the east, as Figure 4.4 demonstrates. If this contention is true, then it was easy for surplus doctoring capacity to develop in west Lancashire at the same time as there was insufficient capacity in the east of the county – a problem not alleviated by the tendency for doctors to have circuits on which they travelled.[23]

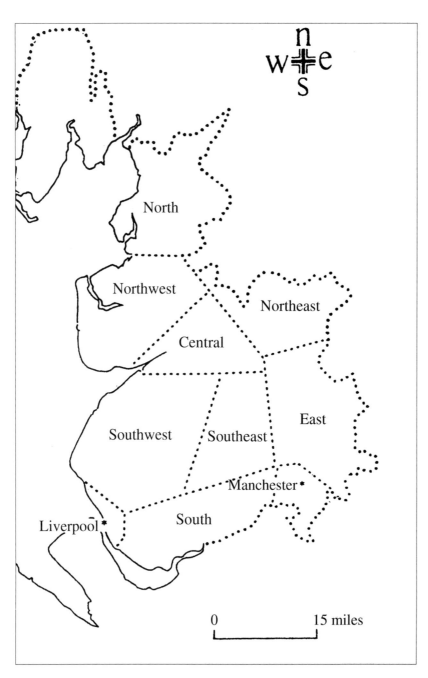

Figure 4.4: Medical sub-regions in Lancashire
Source: Reproduced from King and Weaver, 'Lives', by kind permission of the Wellcome Trust.

Some brief examples will illustrate this mismatch. Thus, in the early 1770s, Aughton had 3 doctors (Aspinall, Plumber and Wade) and by the 1790s this had swelled to 5 whereas the population had hardly grown at all. Two of them were to go bankrupt before 1800. In Bolton 6 medical men were recorded in 1783 and this had only risen to 11 in 1806 despite considerable growth in the population of the town and its surroundings.[24] Benjamin Wraith must have been a very imprudent doctor indeed to reach bankruptcy in this hothouse of notional demand for medical services.

Of course, this still does not explain why doctors did not move from areas of low earning potential to the east of the county. Failure to achieve perfect equilibrium may have reflected discrete information fields in different sub-regions, the fact that doctors in some areas diversified their earning capacities (a subject to which we return below) and reduced their dependence on medical incomes or that some doctors had a particular interest in hanging on in the face of limited economic opportunities, for instance where they had inherited a practice from their father. Whatever the reason, intense competition between doctors in some communities and sub-regions could develop well before the general increase in competition which Digby and Loudon ascribe to the nineteenth century. Thus, in Colne between 1740 and 1760, 7 medical men had circuits covering the town. Samuel Coats was the resident town doctor, but Colne was also on the circuits of John Wilson, William Midgeley and John Parr, surgeon-apothecaries, and under the medical jurisdiction of Richard Oddey, Coroner and part-time doctor. The town was also well serviced by irregular practitioners. Christopher Hargreaves, a barber-surgeon, was operating in the town in the 1740s and 1750s and John Hartley, shopkeeper-cum-apothecary, was based in the town at the same time.[25] That some of these men had extensive patient lists outside the town is confirmed by the diary of Elizabeth Shackleton, but even allowing for this 7 doctors in a town of just 1100 must have spelt intense local competition and have compromised the incomes of the regular medical men.

A *third* problem was that whatever the notional and actual income of doctors, they were expected to have a certain standard of living, a civic and charitable role and a general visibility which could be costly to maintain. The nature of their business also involved doctors in hefty initial and regular expenditure, not the least of which was a surgery and a very good horse. Surplus expenditure as well as insufficient income could drive a doctor to the wall. While historians have yet to really analyze what symbolic tokens of being a successful doctor became necessary at what point in the professional life-cycle, the fact that (as we saw so keenly in the last chapter) doctors tried to put themselves on a friendly footing with their middling patients necessitated consistently heavy expenditure on clothes and entertainment, luxury foods and presents. The experiences of the doctors connected to the Shackleton and Parker families provide an interesting case study. They were expected to entertain their middling patients (implying that they had the house to do so) and to facilitate things like courtship. On 4 January 1781 we learn that 'Baron Cunliffe paying great court to Miss Wilcox at Dr Farmers'. Of course, it may have been in Dr Farmer's interests to encourage a connection between his niece and Cunliffe, but doing so cost money. So did going to dinner, with Dr Farmer, Dr Smith and Dr Turner regular visitors at Alkincoats. Doctors might also be expected to go foxhunting, and they were certainly expected to attend balls and other entertainments. On February 14 1781, 'Mr S[hackleton] and myself went at 4 to drink tea at Mr [DR] Turner's, met all the ladies from Langrey, then we all went to Mr Fawcett's ball'.[26] On May 4th Elizabeth Shackleton records the details of a party:

> the company all dress'd out and smart were Mr and Mrs Turner, Doctor St Clair [Sic], Mr Metcalfe, Doctor Bulcock, Mr Abra Hargreaves, Lawyer Shaw, Mr Shackleton, myself, my own dear Tom [her son], his wife and my own dear sweet little child Robert and his own dear nice little sister the young Elizabeth.[27]

Such socialising cost considerable amounts and might be enough to push a doctor over the financial edge where he did not have independent or family money to back him up.[28] As Figure 4.5 suggests, upsetting patients in a professional or social capacity could carry significant consequences.

Meanwhile, so called 'voluntary work' could also be onerous and eat into the time of the doctor which would otherwise have been spent earning money with patients. When local elites decided to make special charitable collections for the poor in years of high prices or trade downturn, the doctor was one of the first people called upon to help with collecting and then distributing money, given wide connections in their local communities. Even in small towns this process could take up many days, and was especially

Figure 4.5: Letter expressing dissatisfaction with a doctor
Source: Item ZHE/42/59, 'Letter', reproduced by kind permission of Bolton Archive and Local Studies Unit.

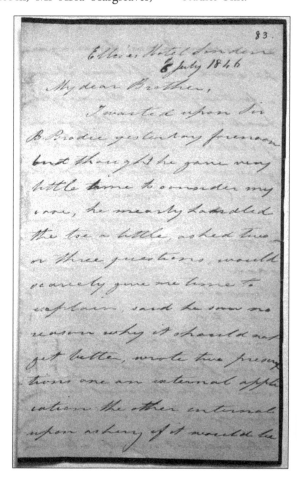

onerous where the givers of charity demanded written reports or registers of recipients.[29] All of this was quite apart, of course, from the financial burden which a generous contribution of the sort expected from a local doctor might pose. Moreover, doctors were also frequently called upon to play a part in local election contests, were often witnesses in court cases and usually filled a number of local public roles such as will writing.

Finally, it is important to understand that doctors themselves were frequently ill or incapacitated. This is not a new observation. As Digby suggests, travelling several hundred miles per month on horseback at all hours and in all weathers must have taken a toll on the health of medical people and exposed them to greater risks of accident. As we have already seen, Richard Kay spent much of his diary complaining about his own poor health. Other medical men were less forthcoming about illnesses but their journals nonetheless hint strongly at extended runs of ill-health.[30] However, the financial implications of sickness have not really been explored in great depth. Dr Turner, the regular practitioner of Elizabeth Shackleton, was unable to attend when called on 17 different occasions, usually citing gout. In some instances this may have been a convenient excuse to avoid the hypochondriac patient, but Shackleton also commented on the appearance of the doctor and confirms for us frequent illness. Turner clearly lost call-out and other fees at these times, and indeed in July 1781 he was obliged to sell up, presumably due to his ill-health. Shackleton notes 'Call'd upon Dr Turner to desire he wo'd come and look at my foot on Friday, he said he wo'd. Heard he had sold his shop to a Mr Thompson of Burnley, he did not absolutely deny it'.[31] This sale was simply a variant of the much better documented later nineteenth century turnover of Lancashire practices traced by Digby via advertisements in the *British Medical Journal*.[32] For Turner, the 'Golden Age' clearly did not look so golden.

Being a Lancashire doctor was thus not always a licence to print money, though it is impossible to establish any countywide indicators of medical prosperity given the patchy survival of empirical material. Not surprisingly doctors deployed various coping strategies to protect their economic position, and it is important to review these avenues in general terms. A wife could help both in the sense that she might bring a dowry and because, where she was of sufficient social standing, her connection might be a way to extend business up and across the social scale. Thus, Dr Midgeley of Colne married the daughter of a prominent Manchester merchant, probably increasing his standing amongst the new rich of later eighteenth century Lancashire. Even without these advantages a wife could be useful in the sense that she could be put to work. This might involve minding the apothecary shop, collecting herbs or corresponding with and visiting sick patients on a social level, thus fostering more intimate business contacts. This was certainly the case with the wives of the doctors who visited Elizabeth Shackleton, and William St Clare eagerly encouraged visits by his wife and children to the Parkers and the Whitackers. Alternatively, wives could work independently of their husbands, thus generating an additional income. Some earning opportunities might arise directly from the husband's position. Thus, the wife of Dr Riddough of Aughton made money by selling cloth to the overseer at the same time as her husband was doctoring the poor.[33] And for doctors in straightened circumstances or who needed loans to expand, in-laws could be a useful source of capital to complement the doctor's own family.

Meanwhile, a doctor might also bolster his economic position by serving in paid and unpaid offices. Surprising numbers sat in a voluntary capacity (though they often could claim generous expenses) on their local vestry rather than simply supplying medical care to paupers, as the last chapter began to show. Dr Smith of Garstang was a long standing member of the vestry in 1817.[34] This gave him contact with the shopkeepers and the middling sorts who would have made up the bulk of his patients, but it also allowed him to exploit the grey area between private and poor law patients. Where he treated someone who subsequently could not pay, he had some leverage over the overseer to ensure that his bill was paid. The other two doctors in Garstang – Wright and Rogerson – also took up positions on the vestry, so that in 1825, fully one quarter of vestrymen were doctors. That Rogerson was particularly good at exploiting the grey area between pauper and private patients is demonstrated by an entry for June 1825, which noted that 'A bill from Mr Rogerson was presented for services and medicines for Jenny Witherington – the same to be paid by the township'. However, doctors had to beware of exploiting this earning avenue too frequently. On this occasion the payment of the bill was accompanied by a rider that 'In order to prevent any misunderstanding and objections to the payment of bills incurred on account of paupers. That no accounts shall be paid unless a written order shall have been given by the overseer authorising the same'. This was a reprimand, but its tone suggests clearly that the doctors had this vestry thoroughly tied up.[35] Other vestries also had a problem with this grey area. In February 1829 the Clitheroe Select Vestry noted that

> Robert Booth has applied for relief in consequence of not being able to work from sickness. Mr Sumner is attending him as his physician – he says that he called Mr Sumner himself and will pay him for his attention. The vestry told him they would not pay any bill on this account and they request that Robert Booth would communicate the same to Mr Sumner.[36]

The vestry of Lund had a persistent problem with the activities of medical men, banning them from offering treatment to paupers unsolicited by the vestry on no less than 7 occasions in the 10 years 1815–1824.[37] The very fact that they had to keep issuing warnings is an indication of the success of doctors in making their voluntary work pay. In similar vein, doctors in Lancashire also appear, along with attorneys, to have been a mainstay of the trustee system. Background work to this project has recovered almost 60 incidents of doctors acting as trustees, presumably giving them access to expenses and to middling families who they might otherwise have not been able to court in a formal doctor-patient relationship. Paid appointments might also help the economic position of the doctor. The coroner's jury was one opportunity. Dr Richard Reynolds, chemist and doctor of physick had a practice in Oxford Street, Bolton, and augmented his income by £10 annually through his service on the jury.[38] Jails also offered opportunities for medical men to act as retained consultants and there were lucrative opportunities in infirmaries and dispensaries too.[39] Getting a 'good character' from prominent patients could be vital in realising the economic opportunities offered by such paid positions, and Figure 4.6 suggests some of the tensions that could arise where patients came into conflict over the people that they were advancing.

A further strategy was for doctors to develop networks of cross-referral to deal with the fact that Lancashire patients were very much prone to seek several medical opinions about the same condition. We saw this sort of practice played out in the Shackleton diaries in the last chapter. There are numerous other examples.[40] Such observations are hardly new; what was different about Lancashire was not only that networks of this sort developed, but that in most of the significant Lancashire towns doctors crowded together in the same area, creating a medical district. Bolton provides a particularly good example. In 1824, *Baines Directory* records 11 medical men; of these 8 lived and worked in Deansgate and 5 lived and worked almost right next door to each other.[41] Moreover, Deansgate seems to have been the haven for medical men for at least two generations. Dr Robert Taylor took a lease of a house in Deansgate from Joseph and Sarah Lowe in 1807, while the unfortunate Benjamin Wraith was there in the 1780s and 1790s.[42] Even further back, John Lancaster, apothecary, took a lease for a dwelling house and shop in Deansgate in October 1765.[43] Deansgate was not to lose its medical flavour, though other medical districts also developed as the town expanded rapidly and the tendency to create middle class squares increased. In a Directory of 1843, for instance, 47 medical practitioners and 1 midwife are named, with 12 living in or around Deansgate, 8 in Bradshaw Gate, 5 in Mawdsley Street and 6 in Nelson Square. New additions to the medical profession in the town actively sought out accommodation in these areas.[44] Thus, James Morris, a druggist, leased what had been Benjamin

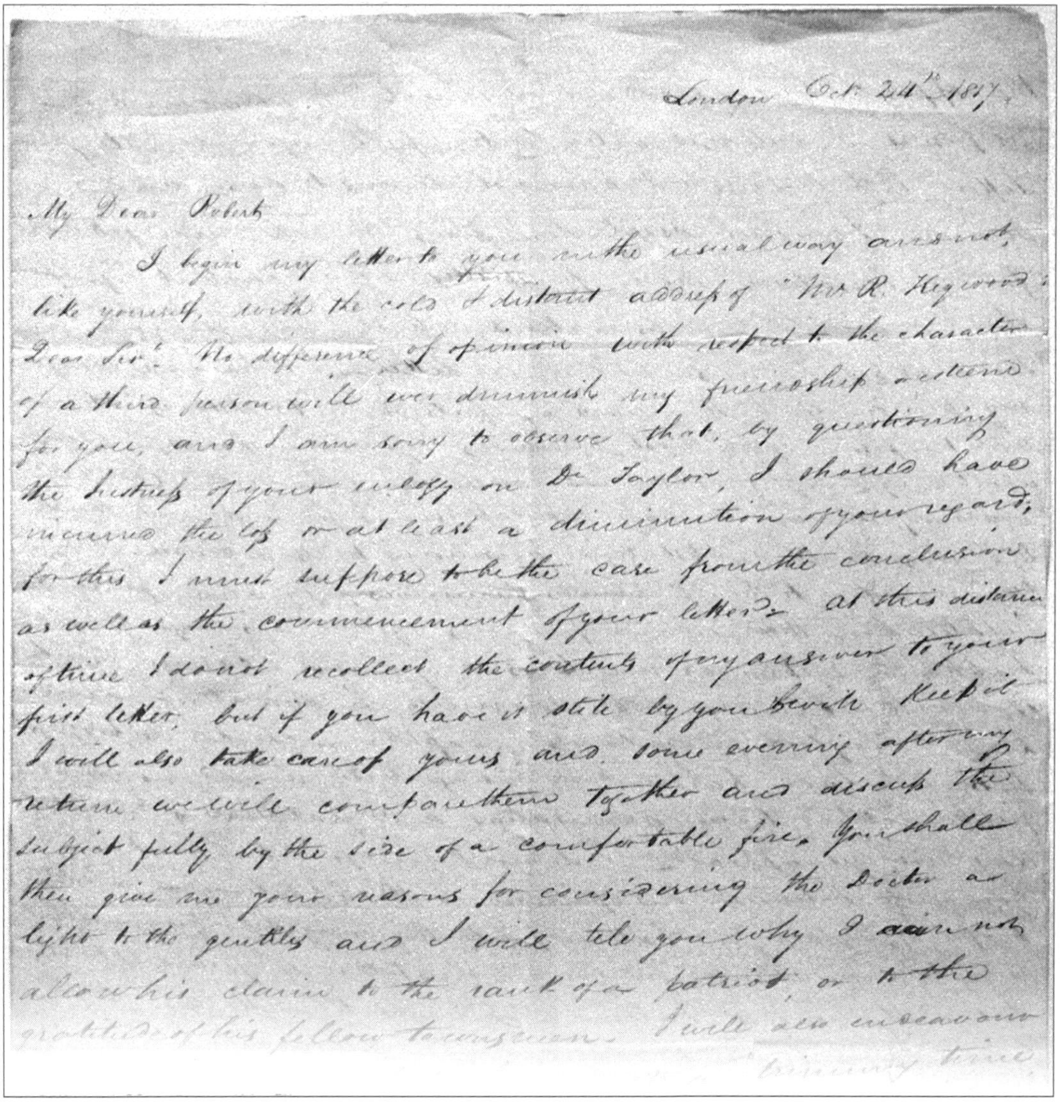

Figure 4.6: Letter outlining conflict over references for a doctor
Source: Item ZHE/13/67, 'Letter', reproduced by kind permission of Bolton Archive and Local Studies Unit.

Wraith's shop for 21 years at £100 per annum in May 1852.[45] Other towns with a different character could boast similar concentration. In 1824, Blackpool had no resident medical people. By 1848 there were 7 medical men, 5 of them in or around South Beach.[46] Clitheroe in 1824 had just 2 medical men, but by 1848 this had grown to 13 (including 2 veterinary surgeons) with 4 resident in or around King Street and 5 in or around Market Square.[47] There were sound economic reasons for this strategy. Concentration allowed doctors to bargain good rents from landlords, made credit easier and allowed doctors to lend between themselves. In Lancashire even more than elsewhere, income came in spurts, leaving some doctor's with cash flow problems at the same time as others had more money than they knew what to do with. As we will see, many doctors used such lump sums to diversify, but they may also have lent to their neighbours. Moreover, as an extension of this grouping tendency, it is likely (though historians have largely failed to explore the issue) that doctors entered into agreements with other branches of the medical profession in order to swap patients, get cheaper medicines or mark out territories. Apothecaries, chemists and druggists were particularly fertile territory for such agreements, but so too were medical staff of workhouses, infirmaries and charitable hospitals and other people such as schoolmasters.

Lancashire doctors also sought to protect themselves economically by diversifying their income streams. While Digby acknowledges that physicians in particular might make extra money via publishing, this particular response to the fragility of income from doctoring has remained almost completely unexplored. Yet in Lancashire it was very important. Some Lancashire doctors published medical books of course, but more frequently (and more lucratively), they published guide books, directories and town histories. So far, 46 different publications by Lancashire doctors outside the cities have been identified by this author. The very mobility of doctors might also offer them alternative income opportunities. William St Clare acted as a paid rent collector and housing agent for the Parker family, while Dr Midgeley from Colne and Dr Hoyle from Cowpe were both paid by the poor law to distribute lump sum payments to township paupers who lived elsewhere.[48] A further short-term response to economic pressure was, as Digby makes clear, to take on apprentices or to undertake formal and informal teaching. Figure 4.7 is a reproduction of a nineteenth century apprenticeship agreement.

In the longer term, medical men might diversify into property and farming. Thomas Boardman of Little Lever, an early eighteenth century apothecary, offered mortgages on land in the area and subsequently assigned such mortgages to meet his own debts when times were hard.[49] Over a century later, Henry Hatton, surgeon of Bolton, was using his lump sum payments in exactly the same way.[50] Wills also provide evidence of considerable property accumulation amongst doctors as a coping and diversification strategy, notwithstanding the impact of ante-mortem property disposals prior to death. As early as 1724, the will of Dr Samuel Scholes, apothecary, left bequests of property in Little Lever and a considerable estate in Derbyshire.[51]

Yet, what remained central to the economic prosperity of the Lancashire doctor as much as his provincial counterparts elsewhere was his ability to judge his fee structure well and to mark out and cultivate consistently a 'territory'. Fee structure was a problem for many doctors. Some conduct books stipulated accepted fees, but for the surgeon-apothecary an ability to judge the market was a difficult skill. Some of

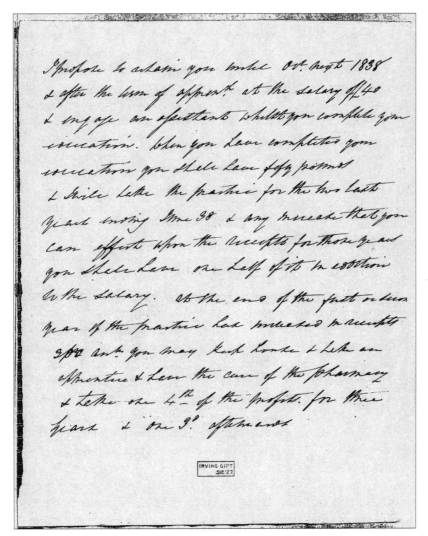

Figure 4.7:
Agreement on
appointment of an
apprentice
Source: Item
ZCR/57/2, 'Letter',
reproduced by kind
permission of Bolton
Archive and Local
Studies Unit.

the uncertainty might be removed by combining with other medical men to agree a scale of fees so that practitioners did not undercut each other. For much of the 1830s, the six medical regulars in St Helens agreed annually a scale of fees for visits to patients (between 1s. and 2s. 6d. depending upon distance and time of day or night) and for treatments ranging from tooth extraction through enemas and to amputations. Such agreements gave the cost-conscious patients of the west of the county little reason to shop around. However, they were also fragile. When a medical man moved to the town from Parr in 1839 and refused to be part of the scheme, it collapsed.[52] An alternative to agreeing fee schedules for visits and individual complaints was to agree a fee schedule related to notional patients income. Thus, on 5 November, 1819, the medical men of Blackburn agreed a set of fees for visits which ranged between 3d. for those with an income of less than £25, to 6d. for those with income of £50–£100 and unlimited fees for those with income of £100+.[53] However, in most places we have no evidence that such agreements were ever in force, and fees were determined by what a doctor thought the market might bear. This issue is revisited in section three.

Meanwhile, a well-judged fee structure was only half of the story. The economically secure doctor was the one who garnered enough patients and visited them sufficiently frequently to ensure that he obtained a relatively constant stream of income from bills that were paid late. A successful doctor would take four key actions. First, as chapter three showed, he would have established a circuit or territory based upon topography, the reputation of the doctor himself and the basic wealth of local communities. As Digby has demonstrated, the size of the territory varied widely even within counties or areas, ranging from a couple of miles in some of the largest urban areas or spa towns, to five miles and up to 20 miles in relatively sparsely populated or poor areas. She makes a distinction between a home territory where a practitioner might expect to garner much of the medical business and an extended territory where he might face competition from other doctors whose circuit overlapped with his own.[54] Once he had a notional circuit, the second task for an aspirant doctor was to extend and stabilise his patient base within the circuit, particularly within his home territory. This might include seeing patients across the social spectrum, but it very definitely involved courting the custom of middling patients, as the last chapter began to suggest.

Nurturing these relationships might take the forms outlined in the last chapter, but doctors might also adopt more subtle methods. Elizabeth Shackleton's regular doctor, Dr Turner, seems to have maintained his role, despite an awkwardness with company, because he was good at playing off Shackleton against other middling families. When he called, he plainly made a point of telling her that he was on the way to somebody important. Baron Cunliffe, one of east Lancashire's most prominent landowners, or James Barcroft of Clitheroe castle are two of the most mentioned people. Of course, the Shackleton example demonstrates the third task of the aspirant doctor. For key families he had to seek to visit as frequently as possible on paid visits but without overdoing it. When one reads enough diaries, there is a constant suspicion, shared by doctors such as Richard Kay and many patients, that doctors made and charged for unnecessary visits and may actually have encouraged a culture of hypochondria.[55] Finally, Digby suggests, it was important for doctors to keep out or at least marginalise potential opposition. The most successful Lancashire doctors in this respect were those who realised and exploited the fact that the medical marketplace was divided in other ways than simply by class, income and space. It was also divided by religion. Catholics and nonconformist groups prospered in the county and a

doctor who was either nonconformist or who came to be trusted by
nonconformists could look forward to a lucrative captive market.[56]

The vast empirical work that needs to be undertaken to put flesh onto
these speculative bones will take many years to assemble. However, a
detailed discussion of the economic position of a single doctor can do a
lot to elaborate these general conclusions. The account book of Dr
Loxham of Poulton provides us with a unique opportunity to conduct
such an analysis.

3. *A Lancashire case study*

As we have seen, Dr Loxham was active between the 1750s and early
1800s, and his account book survives from the 1750s to the 1780s.[57] Since
his practice encompassed one of the most under-doctored parts of an
under-doctored county in the supposed 'golden age' of the surgeon-
apothecary, his experiences may reveal much about the complexities of
making a medical living. Previous chapters have shown that Loxham had
a wide core and peripheral territory. It was not unusual for him to travel
20 miles for the benefit of relatively ordinary patients. In turn, he treated
people across the social spectrum and appears to have been retained on a
casual basis by at least eight parishes and townships to doctor their poor,
as map 3 illustrates.[58]

In numerical terms, cases of childbirth dominated his casebook, but
more widely it is clear that Loxham was a general surgeon-apothecary,
diagnosing and treating across the disease and accident spectrum *and*
offering advice to his middling patients in particular. What sort of living
did Loxham make from this practice? His account book at first glance
provides us with a unique Lancashire opportunity to analyze the
economics of doctoring. Figure 4.8 reproduces a page of the manuscript.

Yet, this book is a very complicated document. Rather than being date
ordered or organised alphabetically, the book details case histories of
patients (with treatments and nominal charges) on a seemingly random
basis. Moreover, while some case histories are set out in full on one or
more pages, others (particularly the histories of important patients such
as the Hornbys) are spread in chunks throughout the account book. The
situation is further complicated by the fact that Loxham mixes up his
accounts for patients with the account of wages paid to his domestic
servants, accounts for domestic and farm consumption, and money
lending activities of various sorts. Nor is Loxham's fee structure easy to
pin down. Figure 4.9 records the highest and lowest fees charged for
some indicative illness types.

Compared to some nineteenth century urban charging systems, the
range of these fees for each complaint is considerable.[59] The range does
not, however, reflect any simple tendency for Loxham to charge poor

Map 3: Location of
the townships
retaining Dr Loxham.
Map drawn by Chris
Beacock.

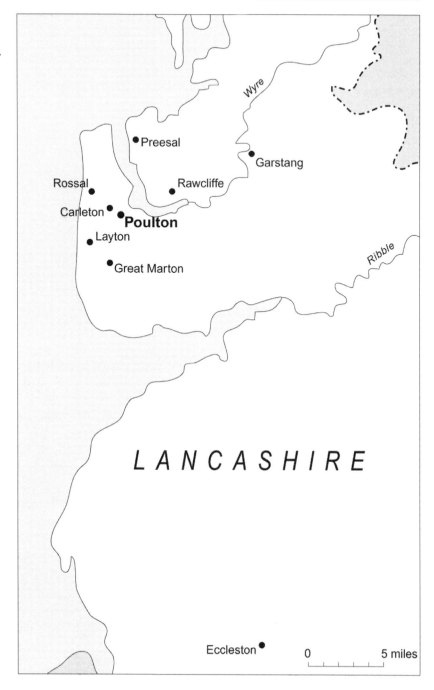

people less and richer people more. That he charged his most socially
prominent patients more is not to be denied. The Hornbys, for instance,
were usually charged £1 or more for a visit, while most visits recorded in
the account book cost only 2s. 6d. Other than this, however, there appears

to be little distinction between labouring families, the labour aristocracy, professionals and the minor gentry who made up the bulk of his patients. At the other end of the social and economic spectrum – the poor – Loxham adopted a sliding scale of charges for certain conditions such as childbirth, broken bones and toothache. Such scales are familiar from the work of Digby and Loudon, but we have few examples of a sliding scale as complicated as that employed by Loxham. His account book makes a distinction between three groups of less well-off people, noting respectively those who were 'poor', 'very poor' and 'paupers'. The poor and the very poor (by implication those unsupported via poor law allowances) qualified for the lowest charges. In the case of childbirth these two groups would be charged between 5s. and 5s 6d. for attendance and medicines, whereas the wives of working men were generally charged 10s. 6d. and the families of middling women might be charged upwards of 20s. Bone setting attracted a similar sliding scale, with poor and very poor people paying less than a fifth of the cost recorded for middling families for similar conditions, and less than paupers. Such cases represent a very small number of Loxham's patients, however, and even amongst people of the same ostensible social segment, charges could vary considerably for no apparent reason. There was also a slight tendency for charges to vary for the same medical treatment over the lifetime of the patient. We see this most clearly in midwifery cases, but also in the case of fever and stomach complaints. Whether such life-cycle variation and the sheer range of fees charged for individual services reflects the fact that Loxham was building late payment fees into his charging pattern is uncertain.

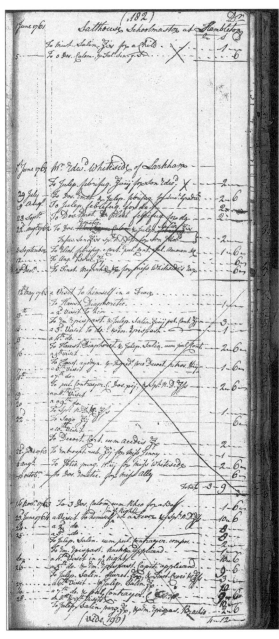

Figure 4.8: A page of Dr Loxham's account book Source: Drawn from document DDPr 25/6, 'Account Book of Dr Loxham' at the Lancashire Record Office, Preston and reproduced by kind permission of the *Lancashire Evening Post*.

Figure 4.9: Dr
Loxham's fee structure
Source: Drawn from
document DDPr 25/6,
'Account Book of Dr
Loxham' at the
Lancashire Record
Office, Preston.

Item/Complaint	Low Cost	High Cost
Advice	2s. 6d.	10s. 6d.
Amputations	8s.	£5 5s.
Broken Bones	5s.	£3 3s.
Cuts	2s. 6d.	£1 1s.
Fevers	3s. 6d.	10s. 6d.
Hysteria	5s.	15s.
Infectious Diseases	10s. 6d.	10s. 6d.
Midwifery	5s.	£2 2s.
Stomach Complaints	5s.	10s. 6d.
Tumours	5s.	£3 3s.
Ulcers	5s.	£1 3s. 6d.
Visits	2s. 6d.	£1 1s.

What these characteristics of the account book do mean, however, is that judging what sort of medical living Loxham made requires patience and some guesswork. Piecing together the accounts suggests that Loxham's notional income from medicine was substantial. Between the 1750s and 1780s his nominal income averages out at between £450–£550 per annum, though there is a clear tendency for this figure to rise during the later years covered by the account book (and by inference the later he went into his professional career). This income level amounts to what a specialist physician might be expecting to earn at mid-career, and in the Lancashire context represents a rich reward to medical practice. There clearly was a medical marketplace developing, even in the Fylde.

Yet, we must beware of jumping to premature conclusions. What Loxham's account book actually records is *not his income but his charges*. The relationship between the two is uncertain and whether an entry with an amount and no notion of non-payment represents immediate payment is difficult to fathom. However, he appears to have recorded with pleasure immediate receipt of money. On 20 August 1756, for instance, Loxham was called out to the Swan Inn at Kirkham to advise a Mrs Smith 'on acct of a copt at her stomach'. His fee of 10s. 6d. was immediately paid. As a traveller we might perhaps have expected no less. Among his 'regular' patients careful consideration of the account book reveals few instances such as that on 22 November 1763 when a visit to Richard Lackerby of Eccleston was accompanied by the notation 'paid'. In fact many of his bills certainly went unpaid for a considerable time or were paid in cash instalments. Some late payments were not too serious. Ann Hodgkinson had medical treatment valued at £3 2s. 6d. between July and August 1760. She paid £1 1s. on 10 May, £1 6d. on 17 May and 10s. 6d. on 16 August, leaving 10s. to be paid later. John Hodgson, bricklayer paid for his wife's confinement in November 1761 in two parts, so that the whole bill was paid within two months of being incurred.

John Bamber of Great Marton called Loxham to amputate his daughter's leg in October 1756. The cost of the treatment and aftercare was £5 5s. Loxham received his first payment (£3) in February 1758 and then two more payments, one in August 1758 and the other in May 1759. However, delays of 12 months in payment were common. Ann Robinson received treatment for a fever in January 1760 but did not pay her bill of 5s. until December 1760. Where a doctor settled his accounts and billed patients once per year, this might be expected, but Loxham appears not to have adopted this system, so that payment delays could cause cash flow problems.

In any case, many debts were outstanding for much longer. Thus, Loxham was called to the wife of Samuel Walker in August 1764, running up a bill of 12s. In December 1764 he notes 'rec'd from his wife 2s. in part of ye above sum and she promised to pay off 1s. per week till the whole was paid'. She did not do so. The next payment (2s.) was not until June 1775 and the next November 1775. Thomas Thornton of Marcross paid £1 1s. towards his medical bill in November 1763, but did not pay the remaining £1 until January 1775. Middling patients were the worst payers. Edward Hornby of Poulton had arrears of £7 13s. by June 1759, while John Baylife of Layton had an outstanding bill of £7 6s. 6d. by September 1759. Mr Richard Warbrick of Poulton received medical treatment between March 1760 and March 1765, running up bills of £3 9s. It took him 5 years even to begin paying. John Wilkinson ran up bills of £6 16s. 6d. in 1762, paid £4 in 1763 and left £2 16s. 6d. outstanding for over 3 years. Loxham's worst middling patient was Richard Lackerby from Eccleston. He accrued bills of £10 between July 1760 and September 1761. Loxham notes 'Mr Lackerby gave me a note for ye above payable with interest dated 26 Sepr 1761'. In fact, he did not pay and carried on receiving medical care until May 1764 when 'rec'd from ym payment £32 15s. in full of this account except 6s.' It says much about Loxham, the nature of his income and the nature of his relationship to prominent patients that he had to wait so long, that such a big lump sum came in and that he effectively had to write off 6s. of his income to get the money. In effect, Loxham was paying Lackerby interest on his own outstanding bill. Under such circumstances, it was easy for Loxham to lose track of what was outstanding. In an entry for February 1757, he notes 'Uncertain if ye above [bill] be paid'. Of course, sometimes Loxham had an interest in accepting late payment. Thomas Danson, landlord of the Eagle at Cleveleys had a bill of £1 7s. outstanding for two years. He paid in dribs and drabs, but since Loxham used his premises as a consulting room he can have had little leeway for demanding faster payment. Most of the time, however, there is clearly a sense in which Loxham's economic situation demanded faster payment than he was able to realise.

The majority of his patients paid up eventually. Other patients, however, only partly paid their bills, leaving Loxham with a nominal debt when the account book closes in the 1780s. Between August and September 1756 Loxham went several times to Widow Atkinson in Thornton to treat a urinary complaint. He entered notional charges of £1 1s. and received 14s in part payment on 6 December 1756. However, the remaining amount was still outstanding when he was called again in February 1758 to treat her daughter for an ulcerated leg. It says much about the expectations of patient and practitioner that he should attend despite the tardiness of payment. Some of these nominal debts he clearly did not expect to collect. Thomas Greenwood of Carleton called Loxham to attend his wife in childbirth and to set a broken bone between 1757 and 1759. Beside his nominal bill of £2 2s. Loxham wrote 'desperate'. Other debts he persisted with, though he was little more successful. Loxham began to treat John Bickerstaff in October 1756 and was periodically called until 1769. Not until 1770 did Bickerstaff even begin paying off his bill of £2 4s, and when the account book closes £1 3s. remains to be paid. In May 1757 Loxham went to David Atkinson's house in Larbreck to sew a finger back on at a cost of 8s. This bill went unpaid and in January 1763 he was again called to the house, in this case to set a broken bone. By March, follow up visits had taken the accumulated bill to £2 12s. 6d. Atkinson paid £2 5s. in April 1763, leaving 7s. 6d. outstanding. Mr Kelshaw of Carleton had medical treatment valued at £1 15s. between October 1764 and February 1765. He paid 15s. towards the bill in February. In December 1765, his daughter Ellen paid a further 10s. 6d., leaving 4s. 6d. outstanding at the end of the account book. Hannah Hodgson of Poulton had medical treatment for a fever between April and September 1760 totalling 7s. 6d. The first and only instalment from the bill (3s.) was paid by her father in February 1762. John Wrayton of Singleton had medical treatment valued at £1 14s between 1760 and 1762. He paid 8s. in October 1763, £1 1s. and 10d. in January 1764, leaving 4s. 10d. outstanding when the account book closes. Even parish authorities were slow to pay. Between 1759 and 1768, Loxham was called out three times by the overseer of Wray Green to provide midwifery services, running up a bill of £2 2s. The parish did not make a first payment until April 1768, leaving 10s. 6d. outstanding when the account book closes. Against this backdrop it is surprising to see Loxham record that some of his patients offered a guarantor or made a formalised promise to pay. In August 1763 Sarah Anyon of Great Marton received treatment valued at £1 14s. 6d. and 'Thos Anyon at Blackpool (her brother) promis'd to pay ye above demand for his sister' but appears not to have done so. Loxham was little more successful with John Fairclough, shoemaker of Eccleston, who called Loxham to three childbirth cases and a nervous fever case between 1759 and 1762, running up a cumulative bill of £4. Loxham notes that 'John Fairclough promised to pay ye above sum in a half year, 2 April 1769'. He does not appear to have done so. Fairclough's bill had been outstanding for a decade and others in the book had bills outstanding for longer. One reading of this case is that Loxham tried persistently to extract promises to pay from his patients but was successful in only a handful of instances.

Still more bills were paid in kind, which might be positive or negative depending on whether Loxham would have had to buy the goods anyway. An early entry in the account book sets the tone for the rest of his career. Between 24 September 1756 and 23 December 1756, Loxham made three visits to the house of Thomas Farr for a 'melancholic disorder' experienced by his wife, followed by a further visit on a suspected case of pleurisy. The nominal bill was £1 11s. 6d. and Loxham records at the end of the account 'rec'd ye value in gloves'. The variety of goods that Loxham received was substantial, though wheat was his most frequent barter.[60] Cuthbert Nixon called Loxham to confinements in 1763 and 1765. In 1766 he paid '10 hands of cannell [a rough cloth]' worth 10s. towards his outstanding account of £1 1s. He then ran up more medical bills, taking his outstanding account to £1 13s. 6d. in September 1774 when he gave Loxham 2 loads of turf valued at 8s. In July 1775 'he owned the above debt before me and Richard Hodgson' and in February 1776 'I settled account with Cuthbert Nixon', almost 13 years after his treatment was begun. In September 1757 Loxham treated George Croft after a horse riding accident. The bill was £1 1s. and he was paid '2 windles of beans on acct' worth 8s. In April 1757 Loxham is called to a childbirth at the house of William Shaw, a carpenter from Marton. In February 1758 he receives a table worth 6s. in part payment of the 8s. bill. William Fairclough, miller, paid part of his outstanding bill of £1 8s. 6d. in meal and seeds. Hugh Snape paid his bill with glass and glazing services, while James Hodgson paid part of his wife's midwifery bill with 10s. 6d. in cash and the rest in 'turn'd tins' valued at 1s. each. Labour services might also be provided. Thomas Lawton of Poulton was a poor flax dresser charged 5s. 6d. for a complex childbirth case in October 1758. In October 1759, Loxham notes that 'he began to attend my house and black my shoes and c.', paying off his debt at the equivalent of 1s. per week. William Miller, flaxman of Poulton, paid his bill by providing Loxham with a potato ground and undertaking the labour to work it. Matthew Fisher of Poulton paid a small part of his bill in cash and the rest in services (mowing, manuring, ploughing) or goods (particularly clover). John Butcher of Poulton sent his daughter Nelly to work for Loxham in his hay field in order to pay off a debt of 8s. 6d. Other patients assigned outstanding debts to him in order to avoid paying ready cash. James Boardman, Butcher, was treated for various disorders in 1759 and assigned a debt of 8s. 4d. outstanding to him from F. Tennant, shopkeeper, by way of payment. There is no evidence that Loxham was able to collect this debt, and such practices hint at his economic weakness. Sometimes, the value of the payment in kind would exceed the cost of medical services. This was the case for James Law of Warbreck, who paid an 18s. 6d. doctors bill with malt valued at £1 1s. Loxham notes 'P'd him ye balance of 2s 6d'. George Thornton, butcher, ran up a bill of £1 1s between 1764 and 1765, paying it off between 1765 and 1767 with beef, veal and mutton, eventually overpaying to the tune of 7s. 3d. Such instances were comparatively rare, however, and what the latter story in particular illustrates is that payment in kind was also usually delayed till well after the debt was entered into. Of course, given the lack of small change in the mid eighteenth century economy this sort of bartering and reckoning system may have made plenty of sense even if neither party really wanted it. However, payment in kind was not simply a reflection of a lack of small coinage since even some prominent middling families preferred to pay in kind. The Poulton merchant John Brierly paid for his treatment with ham while John Seward of Rossall paid his bill of £1 13s. 6d. with cheese.

As Digby and Loudon have shown, doctors up and down the country had similar experiences, though rarely are the payment conditions elaborated as well as in Loxham's account book. The key question, though, is what effect late and non-payment and payment in kind had on his real income. That his income was 'lumpy' has been clearly demonstrated, and that his notional income was considerably higher than his effective income in the years covered by the account book is not to be denied. More precision is difficult unless we make the assumption that bills were paid when he records them. This may be too bold an assumption. A range of best guestimates will have to suffice. Thus, if we assume that all bills were paid on the day they were recorded unless the account book indicates otherwise, late and partial payment (in cash and kind) would have reduced Loxham's headline income by approximately £120 per year. His best income in any one year (and there was no tendency for the situation to ease as his professional career developed) was thus £430. However, if we assume that bills were paid only when Loxham subtotalled accounts for individual patients, the amount of money paid late or outstanding in any year would rise substantially. That there is some logic in this approach can be shown by the fact that, as we have seen, Loxham had 83 debtors at the time of his death. In this case, Loxham's effective income would more than halve in most years, dipping as low as £202 in 1759.

Would such sums have allowed Loxham to maintain the appearance of a gentleman? Payment in kind should have reduced his everyday outgoings, but Loxham's detailed personal accounts have not survived to throw light on expenditure. At some points, however, Loxham used his medical account book to record personal expenditure, and we can learn something from these brief glimpses. The most informative is detailed below:

apl 1758	Capt'n Jno Barrow my landlord		
	to cash paid for quick thorns	1	6
	to Jno Bickerstaffe work at ye sough	1	6
12th do	to Jno Singleton for paveing over do	1	6
	to Mr Hull for 50 bricks	1	0
jul	a load of sand for Marton	1	0
3 sep	to Edmd Brown for mending a pump	2	6
	to Jno Bickerstaffe for work at ye		
	yard walls and c	8	11
	to Hugh Seed for lime and hair5		6
15 may 1759	to Mr Bird for stable rent	10	0
jan 1760	to Edmd Brown for mending pump	2	0
jul	to Jno Butcher for thatching ye stable	3	8
	to James Bordsea and george Dixon		
	for drawing ye straw and c	6	0
	to Thomas Sumner for sewing ye thatch		10
	to Thos Threlfall for 12 threave of straw	6	0
	to Mr bird for rent of ye stables and c		
	as pr rec't	11	7
	[totals]	1 8	1

Clearly, Loxham lived in a basic thatched cottage and had some farming interests, and in the early part of his career he clearly did not have enough money to buy his own property. In November 1756 Loxham records a visit to Mr Singleton of Poulton, recording a bill of 15s. For 7 May 1757 he notes 'I paid Mr Singleton a balance of 30s. which was in full for my lodgings'. Presumably the 30s., tallied with the bill of 15s. which was written off at the same time, means a rental of £2 5s. per annum, a sum broadly in line with the quality of house suggested by the accounts presented above. Not until the mid 1760s, and even then by luck rather than planning, was Loxham able to buy his own surgery. This purchase is detailed below. In the meantime it is clear that despite considerable payments in kind, Loxham still had to buy cereals, meat and other goods. Invariably he purchased from his patients and sought to barter his medical services against the goods. Bradshaw Croft was his main supplier of oats (for himself and his horse) and despite the fact that he gave Croft £2 worth of medical services, in March 1772 he still had to pay £1 11s. 6d. 'being a balance due to him on acct of oats and c.'. This suggests very big bills indeed for cereal crops and such stories are repeated throughout the account book. Loxham also had to contribute towards local collections for the unfortunate. In October 1761, he notes in his account book beneath the bill of John Hummer of Bispham 'I promised him 1s. out of ye above towards ye loss of two cows and c.'. Had his personal accounts survived, there is little doubt that we would have seen rather more of these instances.

These are limited glimpses, and they do more to highlight the difficulties of reconstructing medical livings than they tell us about the effective economic standing of Loxham himself. Yet, there is evidence in the account book that at certain times Loxham's economic circumstances were extremely constrained while at others he was well off. Thus, he rarely had the ready cash to pay his servant her lump sum wages due each March. He paid her when he could rather than when he should, and often indirectly. Between June 1768 and February 1769, Loxham lent Betty Gisborne (his servant's mother) money on five separate occasions as well as offering medical treatment. This he tallied off against the potential wages of the daughter. In March 1769 she was given 9s. 6d. for a year's work, with the rest going to meet her mother's debt. While this might be read as an instance of expediency, the alternative reading, and the one preferred here, is that Loxham simply could not realise the lump sums needed to pay the wages on time and in full. There is also other evidence that Loxham was periodically pressed. In January 1763, a time when his outstanding accounts totalled more than any other point, and again in November 1764, he enters barter agreements with the Fair family, blacksmiths, providing doctoring services and writing off outstanding bills in return for shoeing his horse and work on his house. In short, despite considerable success in cultivating middling patients (or perhaps because of this success given their tendency to late or non-payment) and in achieving a balanced patient book, Loxham could not be sure of his economic position from year to year. This in the so called golden age of the general surgeon-apothecary. He thus had to be an economic opportunist, and to deploy interlinked coping strategies.

One coping strategy was to diversify his income away from a reliance purely on medicine. Over time he certainly expanded his farming interests, using lump sums to buy extra land but more commonly bartering away medical bills against land and the equipment, labour and seeds necessary to make the land work. The extent of his farming interests towards the end of the period covered by the account book are suggested by an entry in the treatment history of Richard Bamber of Little Bispham. On 26th February 1769, he notes 'p'd his son John Bamber for 5 loads of barley which I bought of him for seed'. Loxham also diversified into property, notably taking stakes in the public houses where he conducted much of his consulting, and grasped institutional appointments where they arose. He acted as a poor law doctor for eight different parishes, though he appears to have been solely contracted by none, clearly building up a reputation in midwifery. Such selective engagement with the regional poor law authorities was a good strategy, allowing Loxham to avoid the non-profitable parts of poor law doctoring, such as dealing with infectious diseases, skin disorders and injuries.

As we would expect from the discussion in the preceding section, Loxham was also active in the creation of networks of cross-referral. What was different about Loxham was that agreements with other doctors appear to have been rare in the early and middle of his career; not until 1799 do we gain any evidence from the account book that he acted in unison with other doctors. Given the comparative dearth of doctors in the west of the county this is not as surprising as it might first seem, but there is also a sense in which Loxham shunned such agreements in favour of lucrative arrangements with other types of practitioner. His relationship with the Kirkham apothecary partnership John Cowling and William Hull stands out.[61] Four aspects of this relationship merit consideration. First, as we shall see below, William Hull in particular was a channel for the lending activities of Loxham, who either lent to him directly or to his acquaintances when Loxham visited Hull's shop. Much of the lending undertaken at William Brown's (outlined below) was to people identified by Hull. Second, whenever Loxham was called out over long distances he invariably dined and lodged with Hull on his way back. This no doubt fostered the business relationship between the two, but also had the effect of saving Loxham the costs of food, a bed and stabling. Third, it is clear that the majority of the medicines that Loxham prescribed for his patients came from the partnership. The Cowling/Hull recipe book, as Figure 4.10 suggests, contains recipe's for all of the treatments regularly offered by Loxham, and the Loxham's account book itself provides supplementary evidence of the nature of their relationship. Thus, on 19 June 1758 Loxham 'p'd Mr Hull on her [Ellen Whiteside] acct for pills'. Finally, Cowling and Hull had a patient list of their own and cross-referred to Loxham, especially where they took patients into their home. In January 1762, for instance, Loxham attended Hannah Jolly for a week at the shop, while in dealing with Henry Carter of Larbreck, who appears to have had a septic knee, they called in Loxham four times. Loxham was also called when Cowell got pneumonia.

Given the evident lumpiness of his income, providing him with too much money at some points and not enough at others, it was inevitable that Loxham would be engaged in complex lending and borrowing networks. Figure 4.11 reconstructs Loxham's lending activities from entries in the account book. At any point he clearly had between £20 and £30 on loan, and the entries illustrate that while he had a preference for recycling exact amounts as they were repaid, he was also open to splitting his capital to make smaller loans and (particularly when a big outstanding bill was paid) augmenting his capital to make bigger loans. Much of this lending

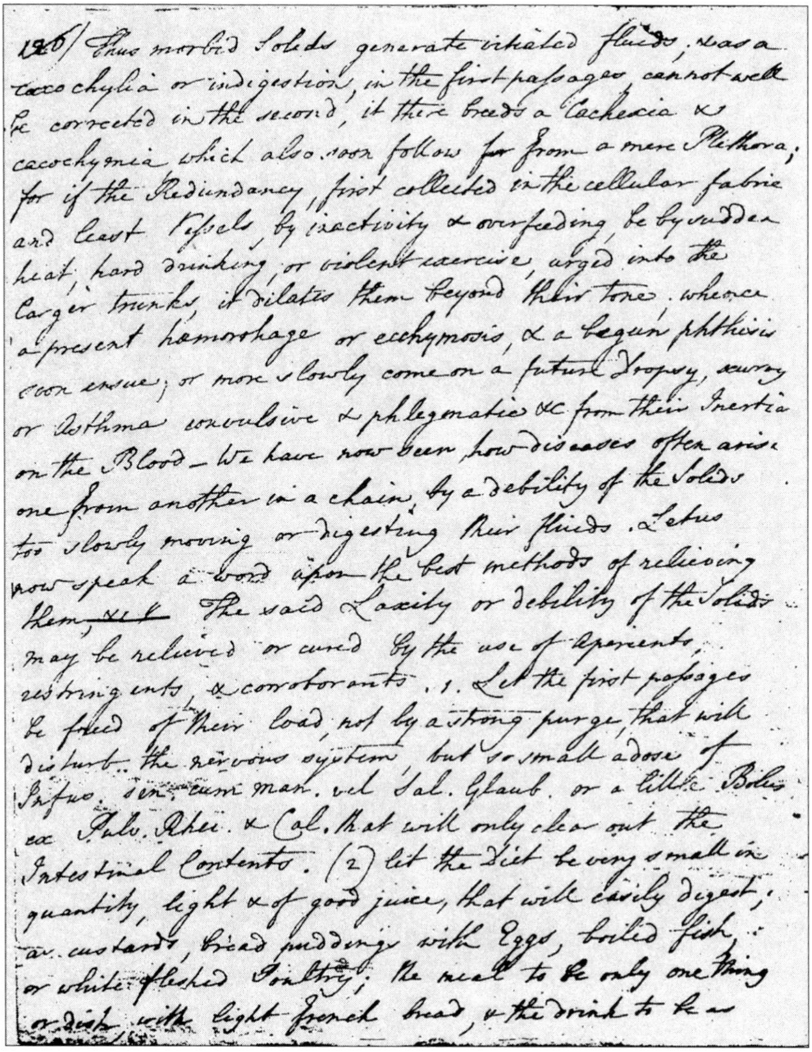
126/ Thus morbid Solids generate vitiated fluids, as a
cacochylia or indigestion, in the first passages cannot well
be corrected in the second, it there breeds a Cachexia &
cacochymia which also soon follow for from a mere Plethora;
for if the Redundancy, first collected in the cellular fabric
and least Vessels, by inactivity & overfeeding be by sudden
heat, hard drinking, or violent exercise, urged into the
larger trunks, it dilates them beyond their tone. whence
a present hæmorrhage or ecchymosis, & a begun phthisis
soon ensue; or more slowly come on a future Dropsy, scurvy
or Asthma convulsive & phlegmatic &c. from their Inertia
on the Blood — We have now seen how diseases often arise
one from another in a chain, by a debility of the Solids
too slowly moving or digesting their fluids. Let us
now speak a word upon the best methods of relieving
them &c. The said Laxity or debility of the Solids
may be relieved or cured by the use of aperients,
astringents, & corroborants. 1. Let the first passages
be freed of their load, not by a strong purge, that will
disturb the nervous system, but so small a dose of
Infus. Sen. cum man. vel Sal. Glaub. or a little Bolus
ex Pulv. Rhei. & Cal. that will only clear out the
Intestinal Contents. (2) let the Diet be very small in
quantity, light & of good juice, that will easily digest;
as custards, bread puddings with Eggs, boiled fish,
or white-fleshed Poultry; the meal to be only one thing
or dish with light french bread, & the drink to be a

Figure 4.10: A page from William Hull's book
Source: Reproduced by kind permission of the Royal College of Surgeons.

went on in pubs. Both William Brown and Christopher Santon were innkeepers, and the vast majority of those to whom he lent money also appeared as medical cases in the account book. We have no evidence of the interest rates charged by Loxham, but given his evident desire to diversify his income stream it would be odd for him not to have charged his borrowers. Of course, lending was not an easy or certain occupation. On July 1 1760 Loxham lent John Butcher £5 5s. for a fortnight. This does not seem to have been repaid though, and it was not until March 1761 that Loxham lent William Hull an exactly similar amount. Nor was lending a consistent policy. The extent of his lending falls off in the 1760s as the payment of £32 from Mr Lackerby in May 1764 allows him (upon realising a few of his investments) to buy a house from Thomas Threlfall in 1765. He

Date	Where/Who	Amount
11/12/1759	Own house	£6 6s.
30/12/1759	Alexander Singleton	£5
01/07/1760	John Butcher	£5 5s.
01/03/1761	Wm Hull	£5 5s.
13/04/1761	Unspecified	£2 10s.
05/08/1761	At Bill Browns	£1 1s.
21/09/1761	Wm Hull (in his shop)	£5 5s.
14/10/1761	Phoebe Gadius	£2 2s.
15/10/1761	Own house	£8 8s.
29/12/1761	At Chris Santons	£1 1s.
16/10/1762	Own house	£9 9s.
26/10/1762	Mrs Rossal	£1 11s. 6d.
16/12/1762	Own house	£4 4s.
07/01/1763	Own house	£3 3s.
27/01/1763	Own house	£5 5s.
14/03/1763	At Chris Santons	£1 11s. 6d.
17/05/1763	At Wm Browns	£5 5s.
24/06/1763	Own house	£1 1s.
29/06/1763	At Gt Eccleston	10s. 6d.
06/08/1763	Edmund Brown	£2 2s.
25/09/1763	At Wm Browns	£1 1s.
10/10/1763	Own house	£6
02/11/1763	Greenwood	£1 1s.
07/04/1764	At Wm Browns	10s. 6d.
22/08/1764	Own house	£1 6s.
01/01/1765	At Wm Browns	£1 1s.
15/01/1765	At Wm Browns	£1 1s.
02/05/1765	Mrs Walter	£5
05/05/1765	Thos Threlfall	£2 2s.
22/06/1765	Thos Threlfall	£3 3s.
18/09/1765	At Wm Browns	£2 2s.
15/12/1767	Unspecified	£1 1s.
25/05/1768	At Wm Browns	£3 3s.
24/05/1776	Own house	3s.

Figure 4.11: Dr Loxham's lending activities
Source: Drawn from document DDPr 25/6, 'Account Book of Dr Loxham' at the Lancashire Record Office, Preston.

was evidently confident enough to contemplate some changes to the fabric of the house, paying Mr Standon £3 for 1000 bricks in September 1765. However, persistent cash flow problems meant that Loxham was often a borrower at the same time as he was a lender. His account book records at least seventeen instances in which he borrowed money from patients, presumably to tide him over income shortfalls.

Loxham's final response to uncertain income was to adopt a concerted policy of risk management and cost containment. Thus, he offset some of the risks of slow and non-payment by simply taking on more patients and treating (and hence billing) them more often; there is a strong relationship between the overhang of patients debtors and the highest number of new patients taken onto the books. His cost containment measures included consulting in back rooms of public houses, rather than maintaining a large surgery. In Poulton, he had agreements with William Greenwood of the King's Arms, William Brown of the Golden Lion and Thomas Dawson of The Brickhouse Arms. In Kirkham he consulted at the Eagle, owned by James Swarbrick, while in Larbreck he consulted at the Spread Eagle. Phoebie Gadie also ran an unidentified public house at which he held surgeries. Other cost containment measures may have included obtaining his medicines from Cowling and Hull for somewhat less than he charged his patients and, given a tendency for their incidence to increase over time, conversion of debts to labour services. What is above all clear, however, is that Loxham was not a particular beneficiary of the emerging medical marketplace or the golden age of doctors.

4. *Conclusion*

The experiences of Dr Loxham provides us with the human face of making a medical living. He was not alone amongst his surgeon-apothecary colleagues in experiencing severe economic difficulties. To some extent his location would have exacerbated these problems in any case. There was simply not the demand or wealth in the west of eighteenth century Lancashire to support a vibrant and profitable medical culture. Nor was there the will amongst patients. However, many of Loxham's economic problems stem from factors common to all doctors – late and non-payment, the need to fund an expensive social life, middling patients who might refer to several medical men and treat themselves, all at the same time. This said, Loxham survived what must have been extreme cash flow problems. In his will dated April 1803 he bequeathed all of his estate to four surviving children. And while the nature of the estate is not elaborated, the fact that his will was witnessed by John Nickson and Edward Slater, Loxham's doctoring competition in Poulton, suggests that he had at least obtained local recognition.[62]

Notes

1. See A. Digby, *Making a Medical Living: Doctors and Patients in the English Market for Medicine, 1720–1911* (Cambridge University Press, 1994) and I. Loudon, 'I'd rather have been a parish surgeon than a union one', *Bulletin of the Society for the Social History of Medicine*, 38 (1986), 68–73. On medical expenditure under the poor laws, see S. A. King, *Poverty and Welfare in England 1700–1850: A Regional Perspective* (Manchester University Press, 2000).

2. See Lancashire Record Office (hereafter LRO) PR 2918 3/3, 'Tatham Fell poor law accounts', LRO DDX 28/257, 'Langshaw Collection', LRO PR 2095, 'Aughton

Overseer accounts', LRO DDX 1852/4, 'Ulnes Walton overseer accounts, 1800–36', LRO DDX 1852/1, 'Ulnes Walton Vestry book' and LRO PR 499 and 500, 'Caton Union poor law accounts, 1714–1805'. Also C.Workman, 'The effect of Gilbert's Act on poor law administration in north Lancashire, Caton Union 1800–1841' (Diploma in Local History, University of Liverpool, 1989). For comparative material, see F. M. M. Eden, *The State of the Poor* (Cass, 1969 reprint).

3. LRO DDNw/9/7, 'Poor law account books' and LRO PR 810, 'Accounts'. Also E.C.Midwinter, *Social Administration in Lancashire 1830–1860* (Manchester University Press, 1969).

4. For some particularly good examples, see J. E. Ward and J. Yell, *The medical casebook of William Brownrigg MD (1712–1800) of the Town of Whitehaven in Cumberland*, Wellcome Institute for the History of Medicine, 1993), Manchester Central Library (hereafter MCL) M134, 'Lyons collection' and John Rylands Library, 'Bellot collection'.

5. On these issues see J. Lane, 'The provincial practitioner and his services to the poor 1750–1800', *Bulletin of the Society for the Social History of Medicine*, 28 (1981), 38–56 and Digby, *Making*. Also LRO PR 2918 3/3, 'Tatham Fell Account Book'.

6. Digby, *Making*; I. Loudon, *Medical Care and the General Practitioner, 1750–1850* (Oxford University Press, 1987); I. Loudon, 'The nature of provincial medical practice in eighteenth century England', *Medical History*, 30 (1985), 161–87.

7. One element of continuity between the two periods was the progressive elimination of female practitioners at all levels. See D. Harley, 'Provincial midwives in England: Lancashire and Cheshire 1660–1760', in H. Marland (ed.), *The Art of Midwifery: Early Modern Midwives in Europe* (Routledge, 1993), 27–48.

8. R. French and A. Wear (eds.), *British Medicine in an Age of Reform* (Routledge, 1991), 92–109.

9. F. N. L. Poynter, *The Journal of James Yonge (1647–1721)* (Cass, 1963).

10. This information is drawn from the biographies provided in Bolton Local Studies Library (hereafter BL) ZCT 1/1, 'File of cuttings'.

11. S. Crompton, *Memoir of Edmund Lyon, M.D* (Haley, 1881).

12. W. Brockbank and F. Kenworthy (eds.), *The Diary of Richard Kay, a Lancashire Doctor, 1716–51* (Chetham Society, 1968).

13. J. G. Adami, *Charles White of Manchester (1728–1813) and the Arrest of Puerperal Fever* (Hodder, 1922) and E. M. Brockbank, *Sketches of the Lives and Works of the Honourary Medical Staff of the Manchester Infirmary from its Inception in 1752 to 1830 When it Became the Royal Infirmary* (Manchester University Press, 1904). For earlier Lancashire success stories, see D. Harley, '"Bred up in the study of that faculty": licensed physicians in north-west England 1660–1760', *Medical History*, 38 (1994), 398–420.

14. See LRO DDPr/60/2, 'Trial at large'. His appointment and re-appointment to the Preston infirmary is reported in all of the Preston and other local newspapers. For Bolton, see BL HBO/1/10, 'Annual reports of the Bolton infirmary'.

15. J.West, *The Taylors of Lancashire: Bonesetters and Doctors 1750–1890* (Townson, 1977) and S. A. King and A. Weaver, 'Lives in many hands: the medical landscape in Lancashire, 1700–1820', *Medical History*, 45 (2000), 173–200.

16. BL ZZ 617/Bundle 1–2 Items 8 and 11 and BL ZZ 617/Bundle 4 Items 39, 40, 41, 43.

17. BL ZZ 632/3 and 4, 'Demise and assignment' and ZTE 2/4, 'Assignment of lease'. For evidence of bankruptcy see *Bolton Chronicle*, June 1846.

18. LRO DDPr 17/12, 'Inventory of goods' and LRO DDPr 17/11, 'Dr Francis Carter creditors'.

19. LRO DDb 81/39, 'Diary'.

20. *Ibid.* My italics. The fact that it was left to Mr Shackleton to pay the doctor is surprising given Amanda Vickery's contention that Elizabeth retained considerable financial independence. See A. Vickery, 'Women and the world of goods: a Lancashire consumer and her possessions, 1751–81', in J. Brewer and R. Porter (eds.), *Consumption and the World of Goods* (Routledge, 1993), 274–301. On payment terms more widely see also LRO DDPd 26/40–57, 'The account books of Clement Taylor' and LRO DDX 510, 'The diaries of Dolly Clayton'.

21. See LRO DDBa 5, 'Account books of Frances Bankes 1752–1785' and LRO DDPr 94/5, 'Accounts of George Gillow, 1801–1808'.

22. Digby, *Making*, 156–7.

23. J. Lane, 'Eighteenth century medical practice: a case study of Bradford Wilmer, surgeon of Coventry, 1737–1813', *Social History of Medicine*, 3 (1990), 23–47.

24. BL ZZ 357, 'Physick in Bolton, 1779'. The 1806 figures are drawn from *Whites 1806 Directory*. These figures refer to regular practitioners only.

25. This analysis is based upon a synthesis of the parish registers made available by the Colne Parish Register Transcription Project. Population figures can be broadly assessed from the parish registers and they suggest little change from the numbers recorded in the survey of 1705. See LRO DDbd 41/6/193–94, 'List of inhabitants of Colne, Foulridge, Trawden and Pendle'.

26. LRO DDb 81/39, 'Diary'.

27. *Ibid.*

28. For other examples, see the social webs woven by the Thornton and Wrottesly families in central and south west Lancashire. WRO EHC 18/M786, 'Diary and letter books of Henry and Marrianne Thornton 1777–1815' and WRO EHC 240A/RM 1588, 'Wrottesly papers'.

29. P. Shapley, *Charity and Power in Victorian Manchester* (Chetham Society, 2000).

30. Brockbank and Kenworthy, *The Diary* and WRO MMP 12/30, 'A surgeon's journal, 1843–49'.

31. LRO DDb 81/39, 'Diary'.

32. Digby, *Making*.

33. LRO PR 2095, 'Accounts'.

34. LRO DDX 386/3, 'Vestry minutes'. In addition, where vestry attendance was actually paid, as in places such as Clitheroe and Goosnargh, there could be a direct monetary reward.

35. *Ibid.*

36. LRO DDX 28/257, 'Clitheroe select vestry minute book'. Problems in this area stretched right back to the 1760's. See LRO MBC 608, 'Vestry minutes, 1769'.

37. These records are in private hands. I am grateful to Martin Ramsbottom for allowing me access to them.

38. BL ZZ 627, 'Coroner's record books'.

39. LRO P134/1, 'Surgeons journal'; WRO MMP 12/30, 'A surgeon's journal, 1843–49'.

40. See WRO EHC 18/M 786, 'Diary and letter books of Henry and Marrianne Thornton'.

41. E. Baines, *History, Directory and Gazetteer of the County Palatine of Lancaster*

(Longman, 1824). Such districts tended to be very insular. Richard Hodgkinson was scathing on this point in his letters to his friend James Blundell. See F. Wood and K. Wood (eds.), *A Lancashire Gentleman: The Letters and Journals of Richard Hodgkinson 1763–1847* (Alan Sutton, 1992), 337–40.

42. BL ZZ/554 Item 7, 'Conveyance'.

43. BL ZZ/617 Bundle 1 Items 2–3, 'Conveyance of lease'.

44. *White's Commercial Directory, 1843*.

45. BL ZZ/617 Bundle 4 Item 48, 'Lease'.

46. *White's Commercial Directory, 1848*.

47. *ibid.*

48. LRO MBCo 7/1, 'Vestry minutes'; Rawtenstall Library Rc 352 RAW, 'Poor law accounts of Cowpe, Lenches and Newhallhey'.

44. See BL ZFL/7/1, 'Mortgage'.

50. BL ZMA 7/55, 'Mortgage deed'. Some doctors also diversified into the weaving business. See WRO DDX E1 Box 237, 'Plan of house and weaving shop'.

51. BL ZFL 5/10, 'Will'.

52. Digby, *Making*, 163.

53. *Ibid*, 149.

54. *Ibid*, 112–15. She has also suggested (p.111) that concern with a territory was something which developed from the 1750s and was felt most strongly after 1800, though as we saw in chapter 3 issues of territory had been important for Lancashire doctors much earlier than this.

55. *Ibid*, 103.

56. See M. B. Rowlands (ed.), *Catholics of Parish and Town, 1558–1778* (Catholic Record Society, 1999), esp. appendix 1. Also R. Watson, 'Poverty in north east Lancashire in 1843: Evidence from Quaker charity records', *Local Population Studies*, 55 (1995), 28–44, and LRO DDX 1863, 'Records of the Wesleyan chapel in Colne 1827–1861'.

57. The succeeding discussion is based on LRO DDPr 25/6, 'Account book of a doctor'.

58. Though there was little logic to his poor law activity. The overseers of Lund, a chapelry of Kirkham, and not far from Loxham, paid William Swarbrick of Preston for their doctoring.

59. In 1830s St. Helens doctors charged 1s. for a visit within the town and a minimum of 2s. 6d. for a night visit. Bone setting ranged from 10s. to £1 1s. and midwifery from 10s 6d. In Blackburn in 1809 15s. was the floor for midwifery cases. See Digby, *Making*, 98 and 255. Also T. Wood (ed.), *Memoirs of J. H. Wood, Late Surgeon to the Dispensary and Workhouse at Blackburn* (Cardeux, 1815).

60. It was not always easy to value payment in kind precisely. William Cowell of Staining paid for midwifery services with beef. Loxham notes 'rec'd *near ye above value* in beef'.

61. The medical books of the partnership are held at the Royal College of Surgeons. See EG 386617, 'medical book' and EG 386613, 'Medical book'.

62. LRO DDPr 41/27, 'Will'.

CHAPTER FIVE

Conclusion

I started this volume with a review of several of the core generalisations which underpin the burgeoning medical history literature of the last two decades – the development of medicine as a consumer item, to be demanded and paid for in a medical marketplace; the long struggle of doctors to assert their professional authority over diagnosis and treatment of ill-health amongst the labouring poor and middling classes; the continued role for the irregular practitioner in response to ill-health and the rise of the quack; the lack of advances in diagnosis and treatment; and the continued scepticism which some consumers displayed towards the medical professional. I also suggested that much of the local and regional level research necessary to substantiate or modify these generalisations (which are based largely upon research in the south of England) was yet to be done. In particular, I suggested that continuity might be as important as change in the landscape of medicine at local level, that we should be sceptical of the model of progress which informs much of the historiographical literature, and that we should pay attention to the impact which well established institutional, religious and cultural structures at local and regional level could have on the nature of demand for, and supply of, medical services. Moreover, I noted that Lancashire might be a useful regional focus to test these issues given the rapidity of industrial, urban, demographic and commercial change in the county.

The latter focus has indeed yielded important results. Both middling and poor people in Lancashire appear to have lived out their lives within a framework of frequent and prolonged bouts of ill-health, and it is probable that this situation worsened over time, as Riley has claimed. More widely, Lancashire people lived in a society in which risk of sudden death and injury was pronounced. Minor colds and fevers could lead to rapid death, cuts could lead to amputations, and riding horses seems to have been an overwhelmingly risky pastime in the county. Against this backdrop of ill-health and risk, we would expect to see rapid development of a medical marketplace, and to some extent this is precisely what we do see. In east Lancashire and urban communities in particular, doctors were in demand and they took ever firmer control of the ill-health of middling people. Communities like Bolton could boast medical districts by the early nineteenth century, and doctor-patient ratios were considerably lower than they are in those communities today. In addition, other medical practitioners – quacks, apothecaries, chemists and irregulars – could also make a living in these communities, drawing on the custom of the labouring poor as well as the middling classes. In other areas of Lancashire, however, the medical marketplace developed slowly, if at all. Families such as the Langtons actively rejected advice, diagnosis and treatment from medical professionals, and the valuable account book of Dr Loxham of Poulton confirms that doctors on the Fylde made uncertain livings from limited professional and social connections with their middling and labouring poor patients. Indeed, for much of Lancashire the really notable development of the late eighteenth and early nineteenth centuries is the extension of (albeit inadequate) doctoring services to the poor through the poor law. This despite the fact that the Lancashire poor law is usually acknowledged to be the harshest administration in England.

Continuity as well as change, backwardness as well as progress, are themes that run through the responses to ill-health in the county. Amongst all classes, self-diagnosis and treatment retained its importance as a core response. So did irregular doctoring, sometimes via the provision of medicines and advice to the labouring poor by middling families. And long ingrained traditions of doing nothing in the face of sickness can also be observed. Even if we allow for the fact that doctors might correspond with patients rather than visit them, it is clear that professional medical men in the county could have ameliorated little of the suffering revealed in chapter two. The fact that there were so few doctors did not help. Lancashire had consistently poor doctor-patient ratios compared to other industrial counties, both in the golden age of doctoring in the eighteenth century and the more competitive nineteenth century. Part of the reason for this may have been the difficulty of making a medical living in Lancashire. Competition from other medical people, the long survival of the patient narrative and an attitude of medical pluralism in the county, the fact that doctors were not good businessmen and the uncertainties of fee structures put economic pressure on doctors. Using the account book of Dr Loxham, I have been able to show for the first time in medical historiography the detailed economic life of a doctor in the golden age of doctors. To Loxham and to numerous of his fellow professionals the golden age did not look so golden, and by the nineteenth century is was the quacks and chemists who were profiting from the deteriorating ill-health of Lancashire people.

What this study shows is that we must beware of national generalisation and models which assume that all regions eventually reach the same milestones in terms of indicators such as the vibrancy of the medical marketplace. There is a detailed regional infrastructure to be uncovered in the field of medical history, both interesting in its own right and crucial to a more nuanced understanding of attitudes towards medicine, ill-health and the medical professional. I hope that I have shown one of the strategies necessary to blow the dust off of this infrastructure with this study of England's most important county in the eighteenth and nineteenth centuries.

Bibliography

A. Manuscript primary sources

1. *Bolton Archive and Local Studies Unit*

ZZ/627/1, 'Borough of Bolton coroner's inquests, 1839–1847'; HBO 1/10/1, 'Annual report of Bolton dispensary, 1818–1819'; HBO 1/10/2, 'Annual report of the Bolton dispensary 1819–1820'; HBO 1/10/17, 'Annual report, 1834–35'; ZWL 36, 'Longworth overseer accounts'; ZZ 238 1/130/6, 'Agreement'; ZZ 238 1/130/7, 'List'; ZBD 3/16, 'List of subscribers'; PGB 2/1–76, 'Friendly society certificates 1799–1834'; ZZ/238 1 Page 175, 'Flyer'; ZZ 357, 'Physick in Bolton, 1779'; ZWL 73/26, 'Leaflet'; ZWL 69, 'Personal accounts'; ZZ 530/1–3, 'Diaries and memorandum books'; BL ZZ 486 additional, 'Entwhistle collection'; BL ZHE, 'Heywood diaries'; ZZ 387, 'Dewhurst papers'; ZZ 617/Bundle 1–2 Items 8 and 11; ZZ 617/Bundle 4 Items 39, 40, 41, 43; ZZ 632/3 and 4, 'Demise and assignment'; ZTE 2/4, 'Assignment of lease'; ZCT 1/1, 'File of cuttings'; ZZ 357, 'Physick in Bolton, 1779'; ZZ 627, 'Coroner's record books'; ZZ/554 Item 7, 'Conveyance'; BL ZZ/617 Bundle 1 Items 2–3, 'Conveyance of lease'; BL ZZ/617 Bundle 4 Item 48, 'Lease'; BL ZFL/7/1, 'Mortgage'; ZMA 7/55, 'Mortgage deed'; ZFL 5/10, 'Will'.

2. *The Lancashire Record Office*

PR 113, 'Doctors bill, Simonswood'; PR 2853, 'Accounts'; PR 3021, 'Register'; PR 3168/5/1, 'Tarelton select vestry book, 1822–36'; PR 2995 1/25, 'Easington parish records'; PR 797, 'Accounts of the overseer, 1754–1801'; PR 801, 'Accounts of the overseer and constable, 1797–99'; PR 2853 1/2 and PR 2853 1/5, 'Culcheth overseer accounts'; DDX 1554, 'Benjamin Shaw Collection'; DDBl Uncatalogued, 'The Blundell collection'; DDSc 150/2, 'Book of medical recipes'; DDSc 127/2, 'Memoranda'; DDX 190, 'Langton collection'; DDb 81/39, 'Diary'; DDX 510, 'The diaries of Dolly Clayton'; PR 1603, 'Overseer accounts of Alston'; PR 1605, 'Alston accounts'; DDX 1/6, 'Bispham with Norbreck vestry minutes'; DDX 28/78, 'Accounts of the overseer of Clitheroe'; PR 2918 3/3, 'Tatham Fell Account Book'; PR 2995 1/25, 'Ledger'; PR 2956 3/1, 'Annual accounts'; DDX 28/257, 'Langshaw collection'; DDX 386/3, 'Garstang vestry minutes'; DDPd Accession 4125, 'Preston dispensary Mss'; DDBa 1 and 2,

'Account book of gifts to the poor'; DDBa 3, 'Account book of cloth given to the poor'; DDBa 16, 'Account book including gifts to the poor'; DDX 2098 1/2, 'Sick society payments'; PR 2994, 'Sick society books'; DDX 150, 'Sick society of Clitheroe'; DDHu 53/62/266, 'Quack bill'; DDX 12/10/1, 'Grocer's account book'; DDHu 53 82/279, 'Flyer'; DDX 1554/10, 'Receits of various sorts'; DDX 1554/5, 'Catalogue of trees'; DDX 1554/5, 'List of herbs'; DDb 72/495–497, 'Leters'; DDWh 4/101, 'Letter'; DDWh 4/105, 'Letter'; DDHe 62/114, 'Account of medicines from chemist H. Armstrong for Sir T. G. Hesketh Bart'; DDWh 4/92, 'Letter'; DDb 72/492, 'Letter'; DDb 72/500, 'Letter'; DDWh 4/87, 'Letter'; DDb 72/502, 'Letter'; DDCa 17/234, 'A cure for Thrush'; DDGr M 1/6, 'Receit for bilious habits'; DDSc 127/217, 'Recipe for red powder'; DDX 151/2, 'Book of disbursements, 1728'; DDX 274/2, 'Recipe book'; DDX 235/1, 'William Heyns, his book of 1840'; RCHy 81/1/63, 'Recipes'; DDX 576/2, 'The diary of Edward Cooke of Preston'; DDX 28/257, 'Langshaw Collection'; PR 2095, 'Aughton Overseer accounts'; DDX 1852/4, 'Ulnes Walton overseer accounts, 1800–36'; DDX 1852/1, 'Ulnes Walton Vestry book'; PR 499 and 500, 'Caton Union poor law accounts, 1714–1805'; DDNw/9/7, 'Poor law account books'; PR 810, 'Accounts'; DDPr/60/2, 'Trial at large'; DDPr 17/12, 'Inventory of goods'; DDPr 17/11, 'Dr Francis Carter creditors'; DDPd 26/40–57, 'The account books of Clement Taylor'; DDX 510, 'The diaries of Dolly Clayton'; DDBa 5, 'Account books of Frances Bankes 1752–1785'; DDPr 94/5, 'Accounts of George Gillow, 1801–1808'; DDbd 41/6/193–94, 'List of inhabitants of Colne, Foulridge, Trawden and Pendle'; DDX 386/3, 'Vestry minutes'; DDX 28/257, 'Clitheroe select vestry minute book'; MBC 608, 'Vestry minutes, 1769'; P134/1, 'Surgeons journal'; MBCo 7/1, 'Vestry minutes'; DDX 1863, 'Records of the Wesleyan chapel in Colne 1827–1861'; DDPr 25/6, 'Account book of a doctor'; DDPr 41/27, 'Will'.

3. Wigan Record Office

D/D St.E, 'Standish collection'; EHC 50/ M819, 'Charles Allen's commonplace book 1748–70'; EHC 175/ M967, 'Jewitt collection'; EHC/ M786, 'Thornton collection'; D/D 2 EHC volume 54, 'Recipes'; EHC 240A/RM 1588, 'Wrottesly papers'; WRO MMP 12/30, 'A surgeon's journal, 1843–49'.

4. Other repositories

Chorley Public Library, 'Minute book, 1800–1818'.
Cumbria Record Office WDX 460, 'Letter'.
Manchester Central Library M134, 'Lyons collection'.
Rawtenstall Library Rc 352 RAW, 'Poor law accounts of Cowpe, Lenches and Newhallhey'.
John Rylands Library, 'Bellot collection'.
Sydney Jones Library, Liverpool Dispensary records.

B. Printed primary sources

Baines, E., *History, Directory and Gazetteer of the County Palatine of Lancaster*, Longman, 1824.

Brockbank, W. and Kenworthy, F (eds.), *The diary of Richard Kay, a Lancashire doctor 1716–51*, Chetham Society, 1968.

Clerke, W. H., *Thoughts on the Means of Preserving the Health of the Poor by Prevention and Suppression of Epidemic Fevers. Addressed to the Inhabitants of the Town of Manchester and Several Populous Trading Places Surrounding and Connected with it*, Black, 1790.

Creighton, C., *A History of Epidemics in Britain*, Cass, 1965 reprint.

Crompton, S., *Memoir of Edmund Lyon, M.D*, Haley, 1881.

Crosby A. (ed.), *The Family Records of Benjamin Shaw, Mechanic of Dent, Dolphinholme and Preston, 1772–1841*, Chetham Society, 1991.

Eden, F. M. M., *Observations on friendly societies*, Black, 1801.

Eden, F. M. M., *The State of the Poor*, Cass, 1969 reprint.

Gillow, J. and Hewitson, A., *The Tyldesley Diary: Personal Records of Thomas Tyldesley*, Privately published, 1873.

Ginswick, J. (ed.), *Labour and the Poor in England and Wales 1849–1851 Volume 1*, Cass, 1983.

Hollingworth, B. (ed.), *Songs of the People: Lancashire Dialect Poetry of the Industrial Revolution*, Manchester University Press, 1977.

Peat, A. (ed.), *The most dismal times: William Rowbottom's diary Part 1: 1787–1799*, Oldham Borough Council, 1996.

Poynter, F. N. L., *The Journal of James Yonge 1647–1721*, Cass, 1963.

Ratcliffe, H., *Observations on the Rate of Mortality and Sickness Existing Among Friendly Societies*, Green, 1850.

Spencer, W. M., *Colne Parish Burial Register, 1790–1812*, Colne Parish Register Society, 1972.

Cooke Taylor, W., *Notes of a Tour of the Manufacturing Districts of Lancashire*, Augustus Kelley, 1968.

Ward, J. E. and Yell, J., *The medical casebook of William Brownrigg MD 1712–1800 of the Town of Whitehaven in Cumberland*, Wellcome Institute for the History of Medicine, 1993.

White's Commercial Directory, 1843.

White's Commercial Directory, 1848.

Wood, F. and Wood, K. (eds.), *A Lancashire Gentleman: The Letters and Journals of Richard Hodgkinson 1763–1847*, Alan Sutton, 1992.

Wood T., (ed.), *Memoirs of J. H. Wood, Late Surgeon to the Dispensary and Workhouse at Blackburn*, Cardeux, 1815.

C. Secondary Sources

Adami, J. G., *Charles White of Manchester 1728–1813 and the Arrest of Puerperal Fever*, Hodder, 1922.

Ashton, T. S., *Economic and Social Investigations in Manchester, 1833–1933*, Harvester, 1977 reprint.

Barry, J., 'Publicity and the public good: Presenting medicine in eighteenth century Bristol', in Bynum, W. F. and Porter, R. (eds.), *Medical Fringe and Medical Orthodoxy 1750–1850*, Croom Helm, 1987.

Barry, J. and Brooks, C. (eds.), *The Middling Sort of People: Culture, Society and Politics in England 1550–1800*, Macmillan, 1994.

Beier, L. M., 'In sickness and in health: A seventeenth century family's experience', in Porter, R. (ed.), *Patients and practitioners*, Cambridge University Press, 1985.

Brewer, J. and Porter, R. (eds.), *Consumption and the World of Goods*, Routledge, 1993.

Brockbank, E. M., *Sketches of the Lives and Works of the Honourary Medical Staff of the Manchester Infirmary from its Inception in 1752 to 1830 When it Became the Royal Infirmary*, Manchester University Press, 1904.

Bynum, W. F. and Porter, R., (eds.), *Medical Fringe and Medical Orthodoxy 1750–1850*, Croom Helm, 1987.

Chamberlain, M., *Old Wives Tales: Their History, Remedies and Spells*, Virago, 1981.

Corsini, C. and Viazo, P. (eds.), *The Decline of Infant Mortality in Europe 1800–1950: Four National Case Studies*, European University, 1993.

Cule, J. and Turner, T. (eds.), *Childcare Through the Centuries*, University of Wales Press, 1986

Digby, A., *Making a Medical Living: Doctors and Patients in the English Market for Medicine, 1720–1911*, Cambridge University Press, 1994.

Durham, W., *Chronological Notes on the History of the Town and Parish of Blackburn*, THCL Books, 1988.

Fern, J., *Observations on Manchester and its Region*, Privately published, 1839.

Fildes, V. A., 'The English disease: infantile rickets and scurvy in pre-industrial England', Cule, J. and Turner, T. (eds.), *Childcare Through the Centuries*, University of Wales Press, 1986

Fissell, M., 'The disappearance of the patients narrative and the invention of hospital medicine', in French, R. and Wear, A. (eds.), *British Medicine in an age of Reform*, Routledge, 1991.

Fitton, R. J., (ed.), *The Family Economy of the Working Classes in the Cotton Industry 1784–1833*, Chetham Society, 1965.

French, R. and Wear, A., (eds.), *British Medicine in an age of Reform*, Routledge, 1991.

Gorsky, M., 'The growth and distribution of English friendly societies in the early nineteenth century', *Economic History Review*, 51 1998, 489–511.

Gray, M., *The History of Bury Lancashire from 1660 to 1876*, Bury Times, 1970.

Hamlin, C., *Public Health and Social Justice in the age of Chadwick: Britain 1800–1854*, Cambridge University Press, 1998.

Harley, D., 'Provincial midwives in England: Lancashire and Cheshire 1660–1760', in Marland, H. (ed.), *The Art of Midwifery: Early Modern Midwives in Europe*, Routledge, 1993.

Harley, D., '"Bred up in the study of that faculty": Licensed physicians in north-west England, 1660–1760', *Medical History*, 38 1994, 398–420.

Huck, P., 'Infant mortality and living standards of English workers during the Industrial Revolution', *Journal of Economic History*, 55 1995, 528–50.

Hudson, P. and King, S. A., 'Two textile townships: A comparative demographic analysis', *Economic History Review*, LIII 2000, 706–41.

Jackson, S., 'Death and disease in Bradford upon Avon', *Journal of Regional and Local Studies*, 6 1986, 26–34.

Johnston, J. A., 'The impact of the epidemics of 1727–1730 in south west Worcestershire', *Medical History*, 25 1971, 278–92.

King, S. A. and Weaver, A., 'Lives in many hands: The medical landscape in Lancashire 1700–1820', *Medical History*, 45 2000, 173–200.

King, S. A., *Poverty and welfare in England 1700–1850: a regional perspective*, Manchester University Press, 2000.

King, S. A. and Timmins, J. G., *Making Sense of the Industrial Revolution*, Manchester University Press, 2001.

Lane, J., 'The provincial practitioner and his services to the poor 1750–1800', *Bulletin of the Society for the Social History of Medicine*, 28 1981, 38–56.

Lane, J., '"The doctor scolds me": The diaries and correspondence of patients in eighteenth century England', in Porter, R., (ed.), *Patients and practitioners*, Cambridge University Press, 1985.

Lane, J., 'Eighteenth century medical practice: a case study of Bradford Wilmer, surgeon of Coventry, 1737–1813', *Social History of Medicine*, 3 1990, 23–47.

Bosdin-Leech, E., *Early Medicine and Quackery in Lancashire*, Ranold Press, 1938.

Loudon, I., 'The origins and growth of the dispensary movement in England', *Bulletin of the History of Medicine*, 55 1981, 322–42.

Loudon, I., 'The nature of provincial medical practice in eighteenth century England', *Medical History*, 30 1985, 161–87.

Loudon, I., 'I'd rather have been a parish surgeon than a union one', *Bulletin of the Society for the Social History of Medicine*, 38 1986, 68–73.

Loudon, I., *Medical Care and the General Practitioner, 1750–1850*, Oxford University Press, 1987.

Loudon, I., 'The vile race of quacks with which this country is infested', in Bynum, W.F. and Porter, R., (eds.), *Medical Fringe and Medical Orthodoxy 1750–1850*, Croom Helm, 1987.

McKeown, T., 'Fertility, mortality and causes of death: An examination of the issues related to the modern rise of population', *Population Studies*, 32 1978, 535–42.

McKeown, T., 'Food, infection and population', *Journal of Interdisciplinary History*, 14 1983, 227–47.

McLoughlin, G., *A Short History of the First Liverpool Infirmary, 1749–1824*, Phillimore, 1978.

Mercer, A., *Disease, Mortality and Population*, Leicester University Press, 1990.

Midwinter, E. C., *Social Administration in Lancashire 1830–1860*, Manchester University Press, 1969.

Pickstone, J. V., *Health, Disease and Medicine in Lancashire, 1750–1950*, UMIST Occasional Paper, 1981.

Pickstone, J. V., *Medicine and Industrial Society: A History of Hospital Development in Manchester and its Region, 1752–1946*, Manchester University Press, 1985.

Neve, M. 'Orthodoxy and fringe: medicine in late Georgian Bristol', in Bynum, W. F. and Porter, R. (eds.), *Medical Fringe and Medical Orthodoxy 1750–1850*, Croom Helm, 1987.

Porter, R. (ed.), *Patients and practitioners*, Cambridge University Press, 1985.

Porter, R. 'Laymen, doctors and medical knowledge in the eighteenth century: The evidence of the *Gentleman's Magazine*', in Porter, R. (ed.), *Patients and practitioners*, Cambridge University Press, 1985.

Porter, R. and Porter, D., *In Sickness and in Health: The British Experience*, Fourth Estate, 1988.

Porter, R., *Health for Sale: Quackery in England 1660–1850*, Manchester University Press, 1989.

Porter, R., 'The patient in England 1600–1800', in Wear, A. (ed.), *Medicine in Society: Historical Essays*, Cambridge University Press, 1992.

Porter, R., *Quacks: Fakers and Charlatans in English Medicine*, Tempus, 2000.

Riley, J., *Sickness, Recovery and Death*, Iowa University Press, 1989

Riley, J., 'Working health time: a comparison of preindustrial, industrial, and postindustrial experience in life and health', *Explorations in Economic History*, 28 1991, 169–91.

Riley, J., *Sick not Dead: The Health of British Workingmen During the Mortality Transition*, Johns Hopkins University Press, 1997.

Rowlands, M. B., (ed.), *Catholics of Parish and Town, 1558–1778*, Catholic Record Society, 1999.

Schofield, R. S., 'Perinatal mortality in Hawkshead, Lancashire, 1581–1710', *Local Population Studies*, 4 1970, 1–19.

Schofield, R. S., Reher, D. and Bideau, D., (eds.), *The Decline of Mortality in Europe*, Clarendon Press, 1991.

Secord, A., 'Science in the pub: artisan botanists in early nineteenth century Lancashire', *History of Science*, 32 1994, 269–315.

Shapley, P., *Charity and Power in Victorian Manchester*, Chetham Society, 2000.

Smith, F. B., *The Retreat of Tuberculosis 1850–1950*, Croom Helm, 1988.

Smith, G., 'Prescribing the rules of health: Self-help and advice in the late eighteenth century', in Porter, R. (ed.), *Patients and practitioners*, Cambridge University Press, 1985.

Timmins, J. G., *The last shift*, Manchester University Press, 1993

Timmins, J. G., 'Housing quality in rural textile colonies 1800–1850: The Ashworth settlements revisited', *Industrial Archaeology Review*, 22 2000, 21–37.

Tyrer, F., *The Poor Law in the Seventeenth and Early Eighteenth Centuries, With Case Histories in Crosby and District in the County of Lancashire*, Privately published, 1956.

Vickery, A., 'Women and the world of goods: a Lancashire consumer and her possessions, 1751–81', in Brewer, J. and Porter, R., (eds.), *Consumption and the World of Goods*, Routledge, 1993

Vickery, A., *The Gentleman's Daughter: Women's Lives in Georgian England*, Yale University Press, 1998.

Vigier, F., *Change and Apathy: Liverpool and Manchester During the Industrial Revolution*, Massachusetts University Press, 1970.

Ward, J. T., *The Factory System, Volume 1*, David and Charles, 1970.

Watson, R., 'Poverty in north east Lancashire in 1843: Evidence from Quaker charity records', *Local Population Studies*, 55 1995, 28–44.

Wear, A. (ed.), *Medicine in Society: Historical Essays*, Cambridge University Press, 1992.

Wear, A., 'Making sense of health and environment in early modern England', in Wear, A., (ed.), *Medicine in Society: Historical Essays*, Cambridge University Press, 1992.

West, J. L., *The Taylors of Lancashire: Bonesetters and Doctors, 1750–1890*, Townson, 1977.

Wilkinson, J., *The Letters of Thomas Langton, Flax Merchant of Kirkham, 1771–1788*, Chetham Society, 1994.

Wrigley, E. A. and Schofield, R.S., *The Population History of England 1541–1871: A Reconstruction*, Arnold, 1981.

Wrigley, E. A., Davies, R.S., Oeppen, J.E. and Schofield, R.S., *English Population History From Family Reconstitution 1580–1837*, Cambridge University Press, 1997.

Index

Occasional Papers from the Centre for North-West Regional Studies

The Centre for North-West Regional Studies, based at Lancaster University, brings together members of the university and the regional community. As well as its extensive publication programme of books and resource papers, it organises conferences, study days and seminars covering a wide range of subjects. For a small annual subscription 'Friends of the Centre' receive regular mailings of events and discounts on books and other activities.

For further details contact Centre for North-West Regional Studies, Fylde College, Lancaster University, Lancaster, LA1 4YF; tel: 01524 593770; fax: 01524 594725; email: christine.wilkinson@lancaster.ac.uk; Web site: www.lancs.ac.uk/users/cnwrs.

A Fylde Country Practice, 2001, Steven King	£10.95
The Arts & Crafts Movement in the Lake District: A Social History, 2001, Jennie Brunton	£10.95
Irish Women in Lancashire, 2001, Sharon Lambert	£9.95
Hadrian's Wall: A Social and Cultural History, 2000, Alison Ewin	£8.50
Furness Abbey: Romance, Scholarship and Culture, 2000, C. Dade-Robertson	£11.50
Rural Industries of the Lune Valley, 2000, Michael Winstanley	£9.95
The Romans at Ribchester, 2000, B. J. N. Edwards	£8.95
The Buildings of Georgian Lancaster (revised edition), 2000, Andrew White	£6.95
A History of Linen in the North West, 1998, ed. Elizabeth Roberts	£6.95
History of Catholicism in the Furness Peninsula, 1998, Anne C. Parkinson	£6.95
Vikings in the North West – The Artifacts, 1998, B. J. N. Edwards	£6.95
Sharpe, Paley and Austin, A Lancaster Architectural Practice 1836–1952, 1998, James Price	£6.95
Victorian Terraced Housing in Lancaster, 1996, Andrew White and Mike Winstanley	£6.95
Walking Roman Roads in the Fylde and the Ribble Valley, 1996, Philip Graystone	£5.95
Romans in Lunesdale, 1995, David Shotter and Andrew White	£6.50
Roman Route Across the Northern Lake District, Brougham to Moresby, 1994, Martin Allan	£5.95
Walking Roman Roads in East Cumbria, 1994, Philip Graystone	£5.95
St Martin's College, Lancaster, 1964–89, 1993, Peter S. Gedge and Lois M. R. Louden	£5.95
From Lancaster to the Lakes: the Region in Literature, 1992, eds Keith Hanley and Alison Millbank	£5.95
Windermere in the Nineteenth Century, 1991, ed. Oliver M. Westall	£4.95
Grand Fashionable Nights: Kendal Theatre, 1989, Margaret Eddershaw	£3.95
Rural Life in South West Lancashire, 1988, Alistair Mutch	£3.95
The Diary of William Fisher of Barrow, 1986, eds William Rollinson and Brett Harrison	£2.95
Richard Marsden and the Preston Chartists, 1981, J. E. King	£2.95

Each of these titles may be ordered by post from the above address, postage and packing £1.00 per order. Please make cheques payable to 'The University of Lancaster'. Titles are also available from all good booksellers in the region.